What's in my water?

David De John

Contact information:
David De John
davidd@whatsinmywater.com

Published by: Clean Water Institute
708-687-8300

About the author:

David De John is the Executive Director of the Clean Water Institute. He has been requested as a key note speaker on "What's in my water?" educational seminars at municipal venues, private conferences, health and nutrition venues along with providing information to health care providers and medical facilities. The information David discusses in these seminars is based on a compilation of thousands of pages of data received through the EPA, FDA, CDC, Dept. of Health, American Journal of Public Health and more.

David started in the industry when he bought a Water Filtration Dealership in Northwest Indiana. Like most people in the industry he focused on selling water softeners as the answer to most water problems. The seminars and workshops he attended all focused on the same things, how to sell more equipment. In fact, on numerous occasions speakers at the workshops would stress that dealers and sales reps should not talk about anything relating to contaminants in the drinking water which could "scare" the public. It was as if there was an underlying concern that people's reaction to hearing about potentially dangerous contaminants in their drinking water would cause them to actually ask: "What's in my water?"

Then, one day David came across a report that changed his life forever. It was a report by the Center for Disease Control that stated that an estimated One Million Americans became ill every year and One Thousand People died due to infectious drinking water. He was so shocked by the thought of this type of problem with drinking water in the United States; he immediately contacted the National headquarters for the Center for Disease Control to verify the report. After they in fact confirmed the information he set off on a quest to gather all of the documented information he could on the quality of our Nations drinking water. After discovering some of this shocking information, he walked away from his Water Filtration Dealership and started Hydro Tech to research, consult and provide solutions for residential water filtration equipment needs.

David continued his exhaustive research, obtaining thousands and thousands of pages of data from the Environmental Protection Agency, Center for Disease Control, Agency for Toxic Substances and Disease Registry, Food and Drug Administration, American Journal of Public Health and numerous other sources.

This book is a bi-product of all of his research on our Nation's water quality and the latest in home water filtration equipment.

The author hopes you find the information in this book to be as informative and enlightening as it was for him.

David is available for speaking at seminars, conferences and educational classes for groups and health care providers.

Forward

<u>What's in my water?</u> is a compilation of research from thousands of pages of data from the EPA (Environmental Protection Agency), the FDA (Food and Drug Administration, Center for Disease Control (CDC) and numerous other governmental agencies and media outlets.

What's in my Water?

Table of Contents

What's in my water?

Our water has changed drastically in the last 100 years. With new chemicals being released into our water supply and newly discovered bacteria our Public Water Systems are constantly being challenged.

I would like to start off not by giving you this author's opinions or views, but with the information and facts being released by the Environmental Protection Agency (EPA), Food and Drug Administration (FDA), American Journal of Public Health, Center for Disease Control (CDC), and numerous reputable media research information.

➢ "Each day, millions of Americans turn on their taps and get water that exceeds the legal limits for dangerous contaminants."
(USA Today, Special Report "How Safe Is Your Water?)"(1)

➢ Over 400,000 people became ill and over 100 people died due to a bacteria outbreak in the water in Milwaukee, Wisconsin about 12 years ago. The bacteria, was not killed by the chlorination process used by the Public Water Supply

➢ "The Centers for Disease Control and Prevention find that as many as half the water utilities in the country sometimes fail to remove the same microbe (that affected over 400,000 people in Milwaukee, Wisconsin outbreak).. The CDC estimates that each year, infectious drinking water sickens a million Americans and kills a thousand."
(CNN) (2)

➢ "The reported occurrence of waterborne disease outbreaks in the United States during 1999 and 2000 more than doubled over the previous two-year period. **(Center for Disease Control – CDC)** (3)

➢ In 2001, one out of every four community water systems did not conduct testing or report the results for all of the monitoring required to verify the safety of their drinking water.
(EPA) (4)

Some people may be more vulnerable to contaminants in drinking water than the general population. Children and infants, pregnant women and their fetuses, the frail elderly, people undergoing chemotherapy or living with HIV/AIDS, and transplant patients can be particularly at risk for infections. If you have special health care needs, consider taking additional precautions with your drinking water.....
(EPA) (5)

➢ "After reviewing thousands of pages of data obtained through the EPA, we found there were 14,435 violations from "Water Supply Systems" for health based standards in 2003. There were also violations for: Arsenic, E.coli, Fecal Coliform Bacteria, Lead, and more... We also found over 50 Public Water Supply Systems in Illinois alone exceeding the Maximum Contaminant Level for Radium 226 & 228 violating the EPA Drinking Water Standards".
(David De John – Hydro Tech) (6)

➢ An examination of 65 of the 3,000 largest utilities found cities are "manipulating the results of tests used to detect lead in water, violating federal law and putting millions of Americans at risk," The Washington Post said. More

> than 250 major cities currently exceed the EPA's lead standards, and many of them have been deceptive, or even fraudulent in their reporting of the problems. **(NBC nightly news)** (7)

> NOTICE: EPA is aware of inaccuracies and underreporting of some data in the Safe Drinking Water information System. We are working with the states to improve the quality of the data. **(Environmental Protection Agency)** (8)

> "Political appointees at the Environmental Protection Agency (EPA) raised the acceptable level of Fluoride in drinking water from 1.2 ppm to 4 ppm, *over objections from their agency scientists...* 7,000 EPA union employees and the unions jumped into the debate. (arguing against the increased levels) **(Time Magazine)** (9)

> "...fluoride (that is added to municipal water) is a hazardous waste product...for which there is substantial evidence of adverse health effects and, contrary to public perception, virtually no evidence of significant benefits," **(Dr. William Hirzy, Vice President, Chapter 280 of the National Treasury Employees Union, EPA headquarters in Washington, D.C.)** (10) (the EPA employees union)

> Reports show that the wastewater treatment facilities can not remove antibiotics and pharmaceuticals from water from industrial waste water discharge or from human excretion. These contaminants can be present in the water the wastewater treatment facilities are releasing back into the water supply or soil. **(David De John – Hydro Tech)** (11)

3

> "Local 2050 of the National Federation of Federal Employees, which represents ALL scientists, engineers and other professionals at EPA Headquarters in Washington, have voted unanimously to co-sponsor a citizens petition to prevent fluoridation of California's waters. A growing body of scientific research suggests that long-term fluoride consumption may cause numerous health problems, ranging from cancer and impaired brain function to brittle bones and fluorosis." (EPA) (12)

How have contaminants been entering our water supplies?

Chemicals, bacteria and impurities can enter the water source in numerous ways and affect both public water supplies and private water supplies (private wells).

Following is the EPA's list of some of the biggest threats to our drinking water supply.
(The EPA Safe Drinking Water Act poster 2002):

> ➤ STORMWATER RUNOFF IS THE SINGLE BIGGEST THREAT TO THE HEALTH OF OUR WATERWAYS. As water washes over driveways, streets and yards, it picks up nutrients, pollutants and litter and deposits them in surface waters or introduces them into ground water.

> ➤ We apply 67 MILLION POUNDS OF PESTICIDES to lawns, some of which leaches into ground water or pollutes rivers, lakes and streams every year.

> ➤ Do-it yourselfers drain about 220 MILLION GALLONS OF USED OIL from their cars, but less than 33 million gallons of this used oil is recycled.

> ➤ We drive more than 200 MILLION PASSENGER CARS AND LIGHT TRUCKS ALMOST 2 TRILLION MILES EVERY YEAR THAT ACCOUNT FOR ABOUT 50% OF AIR POLLUTION nationwide, and produce <u>ACID RAIN</u> that pollutes surfaced water and leaches into ground water.

> ➤ WE PRODUCE MORE THAN 230 MILLION TONS OF MUNICIPAL SOLID WASTE ANNUALLY – approximately 4.6 POUNDS OF TRASH OR GARBAGE PER PERSON PER DAY – that contains

bacteria, nitrates, viruses, synthetic detergents and household chemicals.

> AT LEAST ONE-THIRD OF THE U.S. POPULATION uses septic systems, that discharge MORE THAN 1 TRILLION GALLONS OF HOUSEHOLD WASTEWATER containing bacteria, viruses, nitrates, drugs and hormones, below the ground's surface directly or indirectly into ground water resources every year.

> Nearly HALF A MILLION ANIMAL FACTORY FARMS PRODUCE 130 TIMES THE AMOUNT OF WASTE OF THE HUMAN POPULATION EVERY YEAR and are a potential source of bacteria, viruses, nitrates, and animal steroids.

> There are more than 12 MILLION RECREATIONAL AND HOUSE BOATS AND 10,000 BOAT MARINAS that may release pollutants such as solvents, gasoline, detergents, and raw sewage directly into waterways.

Another way chemicals or impurities can enter our drinking water is through the public water system itself. Most water supplies add chlorine and fluoride into the water along with chemicals to stop lead from leaching into the drinking water from municipal pipes. There have been six states which have banned the use of fluoride being added to public water systems and as we mentioned earlier Local 2050 which consist of the scientist, engineers and other professionals at the EPA headquarters in Washington have unanimously agreed to sponsor a citizens petition to stop Fluoride being added to California water.

No matter where the water supply source is, there is the possibility of contaminants entering the water from the above EPA mentioned threats.

Most public water systems use the same filtration process. They run the water through a combination of a sand and gravel filter. This is designed to specifically remove sediment. If you are familiar to swimming pool filters you will be familiar to this process. Most public water systems then add some chemicals: chlorine as a disinfectant (which we will discuss later); fluoride to help in tooth decay (which we will discuss later); and multiple chemicals to prevent lead in the public water system pipes from leaching into the water as it passes through the pipes. This will hopefully give you a good understanding of the limitations of the filtration process and its ability or inability to filter some of the contaminants that we have discussed and some of the contaminants we are going to discuss.

Possible Contaminants in Drinking Water

The water we are using is basically the same water Noah dealt with when he was on the ark for 40 days and 40 nights. There is a specific scientific process to water recycling. Water evaporates from the earth's surface into the air and then comes back down to earth in the form of rain or snow. That's it, it is that simple. The evaporated water never leaves our atmosphere. Unfortunately, when the water comes back down as rain, it can be polluted. The rain water can pick up contaminants, impurities and toxic chemicals in our air as it falls to earth. The EPA refers to this as Acid Rain (yes according to the EPA Acid Rain is real – see the above section on the biggest threats to our water supply)

Bacteria

Bacteria is one of the biggest threats to people who get their water from private wells or directly from rivers or streams with no filtration. However, municipal water supplies can also be affected by bacteria.

"The reported occurrences of waterborne disease outbreaks in the United States during 1999 and 2000 more than doubled over the previous two-year reporting period, according to a new report from the Centers for Disease"
(Center for Disease Control and Prevention - CDC) (13

"During 1999-2000, a total of 39 outbreaks associated with drinking water was reported by 25 states. Included among these 39 outbreaks was one outbreak that spanned 10 states. These 39 outbreaks caused illness among an estimated 2,068 persons and were linked to two deaths. The microbe or chemical that caused the outbreak was identified for 22 (56.4%) of the 39 outbreaks; 20 of the 22 identified outbreaks were associated with pathogens, and two were associated with chemical poisoning. Of the 17 outbreaks involving acute

gastroenteritis of unknown etiology, one was a suspected chemical poisoning, and the remaining 16 were suspected as having an infectious cause. Twenty-eight (71.8%) of 39 outbreaks were linked to groundwater sources; 18 (64.3%) of these 28 groundwater outbreaks were associated with private or noncommunity wells that were not regulated by EPA. Thirty-six (61.0%) of the 59 were outbreaks involving gastroenteritis. The etiologic agent was identified in 30 (83.3%) of 36 outbreaks involving gastroenteritis. Four (6.8%) of the 59 recreational water outbreaks were attributed to single cases of primary amebic meningoencephalitis (PAM) caused by *Naegleria fowleri*. All four cases were fatal."
(CDC - Center for Disease Control) (14)

Cryptosporidium:

One of the most important facts about Cryptosporidium is its small size and composition which makes it resistant to typical filtration and disinfection methods.

The EPA states the following:
"Cryptosporidium parvum is a pathogen found in human and animal fecal waste. It can enter the rivers, lakes and streams and rarely, ground water that contribute to drinking water supplies. Because of its small size and composition, it is resistant to typical filtration and disinfection methods – though the EPA has tightened its standards in recent years requiring public water systems specifically to address this contaminant."
(EPA /CDC/ATSDR) (15)

"Early in the spring of 1993 there was a widespread outbreak of acute watery diarrhea among the residents of Milwaukee. We estimate that 403,000 people had watery diarrhea attributable to this outbreak. CONCLUSIONS. This massive outbreak of watery diarrhea was caused by cryptosporidium oocysts that passed through the filtration system of one of the city's water-treatment plants. Cryptosporidium oocysts were identified in water from ice made in southern Milwaukee during these weeks. Water-quality standards and the testing of patients for cryptosporidium were not adequate to detect this outbreak."
(PubMed.Gov) (16)

Following are excerpts from the Milwaukee (CNN) article –
"…the Centers for Disease Control and Prevention find that as many as half the water utilities in the country sometimes fail to remove the same microbe that caused half the people in Milwaukee to get sick three years ago. That parasite, cryptosporidium, made 400,000 people sick and killed more than 100…"
(CNN) (17)

E.coli.:
"E. Coli. Is a form of fecal coliform bacteria commonly found in the intestines of animals and humans. The presence of E.coli in water is a strong indiciation of recent sewage or animal waste contamination. Sewage may contain many types of disease-causing organisms….E.coli 0157:H7 produces a powerful toxin and can cause serious illness….. In some people, particularly children under 5 years of age and the elderly, the infections can also cause a life-threatening complication called hemolytic uremic syndrome."
(EPA/CDC/ATSDR) (18)

If you live around Lake Michigan you have probably heard of the incredible number of beach closings every summer. In Chicago, Illinois a few miles from where I live they are a common occurrence every summer. In fact there have been numerous beaches closed for days now because of E.coli in the water in Lake Michigan. After a heavy rain the sewer systems can be overloaded with water, causing potential backflow of contaminated water into homes, businesses, etc. What some municipal water treatment facilities will do is allow the overflow of contaminated sewer water to empty into some other source. These sources can be, rivers, lakes, ponds, streams, etc., the exact same places where we get our drinking water. This can lead to increased levels of bacteria in the water. This can lead to extra chlorine being added to the water supplies.

Coliform Bacteria
Coliform Bacteria are common in the environment and are generally not harmful. However, the presence of these bacteria in drinking water is usually a result of a problem with the treatment system or the pipes which distribute water, and indicates that the water may be contaminated with germs that can cause disease.

Chemical and contaminants
Chemicals which have been discharged from industry and other types of businesses can work their way into the water supply. Information is continuously being released to notify the public about this possibility. The problem is the public does not find out about the health risk until after the problem has been discovered. Whether a family gets their drinking water from a private well, a river, a creek or a municipal water system; the possibilities exist for chemicals to be in the water.

Following are a few examples which took place in the Midwest during the last couple of months:

A nuclear power plant in the far suburbs of Chicago, Illinois was "legally" discharging waste water into the Kankakee River. The Kankakee River had always been considered as one of the cleanest rivers in the state of Illinois. Some families in the area got their water from the river, they would allow their children to swim, fish and play in the river. Then, in early 2006 a news report hit the papers, that the waste water the nuclear power plant was discharging into the Kankakee River contained Tritium. As time went on, it was discovered that the nuclear power plant had been discharging water with Tritium in it for years and years. There were numerous problems associated with this issue. The first problem is that the people in the area getting their water from the river had been consuming Tritium in the water for years, with no knowledge of any potential problem. Another issue is Tritium can not be removed or filtered from the water. It emits beta particles only and has a half-life of 12.3 years.

In early 2006 a report hit the news that a chemical solvent company which manufactures industrial cleaning products had been discharging their waste water containing dangerous chemicals into a local waterway. This was also in the suburbs of Chicago, Illinois. It is now suspected the company had been doing this for years and years.

In recent months there was a situation in Northwest, Indiana where a village had been cleaning and resurfacing the inside of their water tower. It was later determined that material they used on the inside of the water tank was leaching into the water supply. No matter how a contaminant enters the water supply, the problem is the residents do not find out about the problem until after the problem exist. Sometimes that problem could exist for years and years as in the cases described with the nuclear power plant and the chemical solvent company.

Does it only happen in big cities? No. You can have similar problems in rural areas, where industry exists. Or, it could happen from natural water runoff after it rains. As the EPA stated, water run off is the biggest threat to our water supplies, even in rural areas. The rain water runoff could collect pesticides, insecticides, animal waste, bacteria, and other contaminants from the ground surface and wash them into the rivers, lakes, streams or reservoir. The water runoff and the contaminants could also saturate into the ground and into the water supply which is being tapped for wells. By reviewing the section in the beginning of the book which covers "How have contaminants been entering our water supply" from the EPA poster. It will help you understand what situations to be aware of in your area.

Of course the most famous and talked about case is the Erin Brockovich story in California. This was made into a movie.

Following is one of the most shocking discoveries I found during my research:
There are approximately 53,000 "dangerous" chemicals in the work place; toxicity information is available for only half of them. **(Baylor University Medical Center)** (19)
Te EPA only regulates about 90 contaminants.

Washington – Growing scientific evidence suggest the most widespread industrial contaminant in drinking water – a solvent used in adhesives, paint and spot removers – can cause cancer in people.
(Chicago Sun Times Newspaper) (20)

Fluoride

The first recorded usages of fluoride dates back to the early 1900's Towns in Colorado, Idaho and Arkansas all seem to be connected with early cases of fluoride in drinking water. fluoride is a natural occurring substance found in the earth and can exist at different levels, depending on the geographical area. What is considered to be the first "awareness" of potential fluoride problems was in the town of Oakley, Idaho in 1908.

The town of Oakley constructed a pipeline from a thermal spring near the town to supply water to the town residents. When the second set of teeth grew in on children who were raised in the town of Oakley, it was noticed the teeth had a chalky appearance and seemed to be lacking the enamel coating. Some time later the teeth started showing brown spots. It was determined at that time that the water supply must be the cause of the children's teeth problems. The town of Oakley constructed a new water supply pipe line to a new water source. Once the new water supply was in service, the number of children with fluorosis continued to decrease. Some years later, research showed that there were no new cases of fluorosis in children in the town of Oakley. Scientific research during that time stated a Maximum Contaminant Level of 1 Part Per Million (PPM) of fluoride in drinking water was a safe level to avoid fluorosis.

Fluoride was first introduced to municipal drinking water in the 1950's on a limited basis in different parts of the country. After research showed a possible decrease in dental cavities in children, a movement was started to start adding fluoride to drinking water at additional municipal water systems. The Maximum Contaminant Level set by the EPA for fluoride was at 1.2 Parts Per Million (PPM), until a few years ago when it was changed.

According to the American Association of Poison Control Centers there are thousands of reported cases of fluoride poisoning every year. These reports are due to fluoride poisoning from ingestion of toothpaste, mouth wash, etc.

"The PTD, 5.0 mg F/kg, is defined as the dose of ingested fluoride that should trigger immediate therapeutic intervention and hospitalization because of the likelihood of serious toxic consequences."
Journal of Dental Research (21)

"This does *not* mean that doses lower than 5.0 mg F/kg should be regarded as innocuous." (Italics in original)
(Journal of Dental Research) (22)
"Political appointees at the Environmental Protection Agency (EPA) raised the acceptable level of fluoride in drinking water from 1.2 ppm to 4 ppm, o*ver objections from their agency scientists*... 7,000 EPA union employees and the unions jumped into the debate."
(Time Magazine) (23)
(Arguing against the increased level of fluoride in drinking water)

"...fluoride (that is added to municipal water) is a hazardous waste product...for which there is substantial evidence of adverse health effects and, contrary to public perception, virtually no evidence of significant benefits,"
(Dr. William Hirzy, Vice President, Chapter 280 of the National Treasury Employees Union, EPA headquarters in Washington, D.C.) (24)
(the EPA employees union)

"Local 2050 of the National Federation of Federal Employees, which represents ALL scientists, engineers and other professionals at EPA Headquarters in Washington, have voted unanimously to co-sponsor a citizens petition to prevent fluoridation of California's waters. A growing body of scientific research suggests that long-term fluoride consumption may cause numerous health problems, ranging from cancer and impaired brain function to brittle bones and fluorosis"
(EPA) (25)

"Early symptoms of acute fluoride toxicity (e.g. gastrointestinal pain, nausea, vomiting, excess salivation, fever) can be produced at doses well below 5 mg/kg - at doses as low as 0.1 to 0.3 mg/kg. These symptoms are responsible for many of the calls to Poison Control."
(WebHealthCentre.Com) (26)

WARNING: Keep out of reach of children under the age of 6 years of age. If you accidentally swallow more than used for brushing, seek professional assistance or contact a Poison Control Center immediately...

Fluoride warning on toothpaste

Lead

Lead has been used in water pipes for decades and decades. The earliest forms of water transporting, was actually from hollow logs sectioned together. Then as advancements in technology grew, metals started being used for bridges (in place of wood) and municipal water pipes. Research shows that lead was a common element in the water pipes construction back in the early days. Most municipal water systems with older water pipes probably contain lead. Lead can be present either in the municipal water pipes delivering the water from the filtration plant to the homes, or it can be present in the homes themselves. Most homes built up to the mid 1980s had lead in the pipes.

There are more and more doctors (especially pediatricians) which inquire as to the age of the family's residence to determine if there is any potential for lead exposure to children due from lead paint used on older homes. It has come to the attention of the EPA that lead in paint is not the only potential problem. Many doctors are now starting to inquire about the type of water pipes a person has in their homes, to consider any possible lead exposure from drinking water.

On a side note, a president of one of the publishing companies I sent this manuscript to for publishing consideration contacted me back with some questions. All three of their young grandchildren had been diagnosed with lead in their bodies. The person went on to say the home the children live in is not that old and they know the paint does not have lead in it. They told me that someone was coming out from the department of health to check their drinking water for lead. This shocked them, and they wanted to know if lead can really be in drinking water. The answer if yes!, In fact, my research has shown thousands of individual homes throughout Illinois alone which have lead levels above the Maximum Contaminant Level set by the EPA. This does not count possible situations with municipal pipes leaching lead into the water.

I think this is a good time to review the water filtration process used by most municipal water systems. Most (again I want to stress I'm saying most, and not all) municipal systems consist of a filtering process of sand and gravel. Sand and gravel can not remove lead, bacteria or chemicals. It is basically a large swimming pool filter. They probably will also add fluoride and chlorine (as a disinfectant), they might add an aluminum oxide as a coagulate (which bunches the sediment together and now being heavier sink to the bottom of the filtration unit); they will probably also add a couple of other strong chemicals to the water supply. These additional chemicals are not for filtration

17

purposes, but are used to coat the inside of the municipal water pipes delivering the water to the homes to stop lead from leaching into the water.

"The Washington Post reported after analyzing data gathered from the EPA that more than 274 major cities currently exceed the EPA's lead standards, and many of them have been deceptive, or even fraudulent in their reporting of the problems" (NBC nightly news) (27)

"The EPA estimates, that up to 20 percent of a person's background exposure may be due to lead in drinking water – and the percentage is higher for infants drinking formula mixed with contaminated drinking water. Lead may be present in drinking water because of corrosion of household plumbing systems; erosion of natural deposits. In some communities lead service lines can also contribute to high levels of lead in drinking water."
(Environmental Protection Agency – EPA) (28)

"Lead is rarely found in source water, but enters tap water through corrosion of plumbing materials. Homes built before 1986 are more likely to have lead pipes, fixtures and solder. However, new homes are also at risk: even legally "lead-free" plumbing may contain up to 8 percent lead. The most common problem is with brass or chrome-plated brass faucets and fixtures which can leach significant amounts of lead into the water, especially hot water."
(EPA) (29)

Nitrates

Nitrate, a chemical most commonly used as a fertilizer, poses an immediate threat to infants when it is found in drinking water at levels above the national standard. Nitrates are converted to nitrites in the intestines. Once absorbed into the bloodstream, nitrites prevent hemoglobin from transporting oxygen.

"Excessive levels can cause "blue baby syndrome" which can be fatal without immediate medical attention.... Avoid using water with high nitrate levels for drinking. This is especially important for infants and young children, nursing mothers, pregnant women and certain elderly people."
(EPA) (30)

"High nitrate levels in drinking water pose a risk to infants because they may cause methemologlobinemi a, a condition known as "blue baby." High nitrate levels interrupt the normal body processes of some infants. Nitrate becomes toxic when it is reduced to nitrite, a process that can occur in the stomach as well as in the saliva. Infants are especially susceptible because their stomach juices are less acidic and therefore are conducive to the growth of nitrate-reducing bacteria. (Adults can consume large quantities of nitrates in drinking water or food with no known ill effects; their stomachs produce strong acids that do not promote the growth of bacteria that convert nitrate to nitrite.) Nitrite in the blood combines with hemoglobin to form methemoglobin, which reduces the capability of the blood to carry oxygen to all parts of the body. This results in the "blue" condition of the baby's skin.
Infants younger than 6 months of age are most susceptible. However, because of individual differences in infants, some may not be affected. If an infant is affected, the skin turns a blue color, similar to the color of the blood vessels located close to the skin. If a parent or other caregiver observes this condition, medical help should be sought immediately. The infant is being asphyxiated because oxygen cannot be transported by the blood. Prompt medical attention normally results in quick recovery of the infant.
In all cases where drinking water contains more than 10 mg/l of nitrate as nitrogen, an alternative source of water should be found for the infant. Boiling the water will not reduce the nitrate concentration; in fact, it actually INCREASES the concentration by evaporating off the water. Water that is high in

nitrates should not be used for preparing infant formula or in any other way that could result in consumption by a baby." (Illinois Department of Public Health) (31)

Disinfectants and Disinfection Byproducts (DBPs)

Chlorine is one of the most common disinfectants found in drinking water

One of the first reported instances of adding chlorine to municipal drinking water was in the early 1900s in Great Britain. It was used to treat the water in an attempt to reduce or stop typhoid deaths. Research shows the first municipal use of chlorine on a regular basis was Jersey City, N.J. in 1908. This started the chlorination process throughout the United States. The process of chlorination in our drinking water showed a major decrease or end to some of the deadly waterborne diseases that were affecting our country, such as: Cholera, Typhoid, Dysentery and Hepatitis A. Before chlorination in the United States it is estimated that Typhoid Fever killed about 25 out of 100,000 people annually. Chlorine as initially used as a disinfectant, but it can also help in eliminating bad taste and smell in the drinking water from algae, decaying vegetation, hydrogen sulfide and more.

As successful as the chlorination process has been in eliminating bacterial threats, it is not "a perfect" disinfectant. As we discussed earlier the bacteria Cryptosporidium is resistant to the chlorination process (this was the bacteria that caused the outbreak in Milwaukee, Wisconsin which caused illness in over 400,000 people). Chlorine can also produce chemical byproducts which can be released into our drinking water and the air we breathe.

"Chlorine in pools leads to breathing trouble in trained swimmers, regardless of past history of such problems, and the likelihood increases with the amount of chlorine used in the water."
(American College of Sports Medicine) (32)

"Showering is suspected as the primary cause of elevated chloroform in nearly every home because of the chlorine in the water."
(Environmental Protection Agency - EPA) (33)

"Disinfectants while effective in controlling many microorganisms react with matter in water to form DBP's. Unchlorinated private well water is unlikely to contain any DBP's....While health effects from exposure to disinfectants and DBPs vary by contaminant, some epidemiological studies have shown a link between bladder, rectal and colon cancers and DBP exposure."
(EPA/CDC/ATSDR) (34)

"...the disinfectants themselves can react with naturally-occurring materials in the water to form unintended organic and inorganic byproducts which may pose health risks.
A major challenge for water suppliers is how to balance the risks from microbial pathogens and disinfection byproducts. It is important to provide protection from these microbial pathogens while simultaneously ensuring decreasing health risks to the population from disinfection byproducts (DBPs).."
(EPA) (35)

The problem is something has to be used to disinfect the water. It is a constant battle for Public water supplies to find a balance that they feel is effective and safe. As you can see there is a tremendous amount of research stating that chlorine can have serious consequences due to DBP's and other issues.

Radium 226 & 228

One of the biggest surprises to this author personally was the discovery of EPA violations by public water systems year after year for exceeding the EPA's Maximum Contaminant Level for Radium 226 & 228. Radium is a natural occurring substance found underground. Public water systems that dug deep wells can tap into this water laced with Radium. Radium is found more prevalently in specific parts of the country. My research has found the outlying far southwestern, western and northwestern areas of Chicago, Illinois is a virtual hot spot for radium. I have found some villages far exceeding the EPA's MCL (Maximum Contaminant Level).

I would like to spend a little extra time on this area because it is found literally just a few miles from my home. Radium has a half life span of 1,600 years and acts like calcium. It enters the bones of the individual where it builds up over the years. Most of the radium can be expelled through urination, but the concern is the amount remaining in the bones of the individual. Municipalities have tried to get the EPA to increase the levels Maximum Contaminant Level for radium (possibly due to the extreme cost in reducing their contaminant levels). Yet the EPA has not budged, they are quite firm on their MCL which leads me to believe the EPA's scientist are obviously concerned about potential health risks if the levels are increased. At the time of this writing there are over 45 public water systems in Illinois alone which are in violation of exceeding the MCL for radium and numerous other cities and systems around the country.

"The human body metabolizes radium in much the same way that it metabolizes calcium. Because of this similar metabolism, ingestion of trace quantities of radium over time will result in an accumulation of radium in the skeleton. Radium that has accumulated in bone tissue decays into a series of short-lived daughter products, resulting in the emission of a number of alpha and beta particles over a short time span....As radium and

its daughter elements decay, the energy produced by the radiation can strip electrons from the atoms with which it collides. These stripped electrons have a great capacity to break chemical bonds as they travel through living tissue, causing the release of additional electrons. The atoms in living tissue that lose electrons become ions at a high energy state capable of producing chemical reactions that would not have been otherwise possible, resulting in damage to bones and other living tissue as well as to genetic material inside the tissue cells. Ultimately, the damage from continue exposure to radium can potentially cause bone and sinus cancer. The U.S. Environmental Protection Agency has estimated that additional lifetime risk of cancer associated with drinking water that emits alpha-particle radiant at 15 picorcuires per liter of water, or has a combined concentration of radium -226and radium -228 of 5pCi/L or water is about 1 in 10,0000. The risk doubles to 2 in 10,000 at 10pCi/L and triples to 2 in 10,000 at 15 pCi/L."
(U.S. Department of the Interior-U.S. Geological Survey) (36)

Radon

Radon can exist in drinking water. Radon is a naturally occurring substance found in the earth. It is a form of radiation. Most people have heard about the possibilities of radon seeping into their house through their basement or crawl space.

While most exposure to radon is from inhalation, it has been determined there is a health risk associated with Radon in drinking water. Radon like Radium 226 & 228 if present in water supplies is usually in underground water supplies. These water supplies can be tapped into when digging for a well. Both municipal water supplies and private wells are at risk for radon being in their source water underground and should be monitored for its presence.

The Center for Disease Control has estimated that up to 1,800 deaths per year are attributed to radon from household drinking water. Showering, washing dishes, and laundering can disturb the water and release radon gas into the air you breathe.

Even if radon is not seeping into the homes through cracks in the foundation or basement walls, it can be in homes due to its presence in drinking water. This increases the potential risk from radon by possibly creating radon gases inside the home.

"In the United States, indoor radon exposure might result in 7,000 to 30,000 lung cancer deaths annually."
(Agency for Toxic Substances and Disease Registry – DTSDR) (37)

Antibiotics and Pharmaceuticals

A big concern is antibiotics and pharmaceuticals entering our water supply. This can happen in two ways: as part of water discharge from Pharmaceutical companies and from the urination or fecal matter discharged from people taking antibiotics or other pharmaceutical products. The reason for the concern is the Water Reclamation District is not able to filter this from the waste water, which can potentially reenter our drinking water supply.

The following quotes are from the Metropolitan Water Reclamation District of Greater Chicago Committee on Research and Development April 7, 2006
"Agenda Summary: Endocrine Disrupting Compounds, Antibiotics, and other Pharmaceuticals in the Water Environment.
The USEPA (United States Environmental Protection Agency) has defined an endocrine compound as "an exogenous agent that interferes with the synthesis, secretion, transport, binding, action, or elimination of natural hormones in the body that are responsible for the maintenance of homeostasis, reproduction, development, and/or behavior."

Over 100 compounds are now considered to be endocrine disruptors. These can be divided into five categories.

- Steroid compounds (estrogens)
- Surfactants (which will be referred to herein as alklyphenol ethoxylates or APEs)
- Pesticides, herbicides, and fungicides (e.g. DDT, dieldrin, 2, 4-D)
- Polyaromatic compounds (e.g. PAHs, PCBs, brominated flame retardants)
- Organic oxygen compounds (e.g. phthalates, dioxins, bisphenol A)"

TDS (Total Dissolved Solids)

"Dissolved solids" refer to any minerals, salts, metals, cations or anions dissolved in water. This includes anything present in water other than the pure water (H_2O) molecule and suspended solids.

Some dissolved solids come from organic sources such as leaves, silt, plankton, and industrial waste and sewage. Other sources come from runoff from urban areas, road salts used on street during the winter, and fertilizers and pesticides used on lawns and farms. Dissolved solids also come from inorganic materials such as rocks and air that may contain calcium bicarbonate, nitrogen, iron phosphorous, sulfur, and other minerals. Many of these materials form salts, which are compounds that contain both a metal and a nonmetal. Salts usually dissolve in water forming ions. Ions are particles that have a positive or negative charge.

Water may also pick up metals such as lead or copper as they travel through pipes used to distribute water to consumers.

Basically a positive test results for TDS in the water can be from almost anything, from harmless matter to potentially dangerous chemicals or toxins.

Skin absorption and inhalation of chemicals and contaminants

"Showering is suspected as the primary cause of elevated chloroform in nearly every home because of the chlorine in the water."
Environmental Protection Agency - EPA) (38)

"We conclude that skin absorption of contaminants in drinking water has been underestimated and that ingestion may not constitute the sole or even primary route of exposure".
(American Journal of Public Health) (39)

The Environmental Protection Agency (EPA) in an effort to assure a minimum of .2 ppm of Chlorine to the last house on the water main, recently "increased" the maximum level of Chlorine from 1.5 ppm to 4 ppm. In comparison the maximum level of Chlorine in public swimming pools is 3 ppm set by the Center for Disease Control. This means the level of chlorine in your drinking water could actually exceed the level of chlorine in public swimming pools which would have to be closed.

To understand just how much and fast contaminants in our water can be absorbed through our skin, try the following experiment.

Buy a chemical swimming pool chlorine test kit.
1 - Fill a glass to about one inch from the top with tap water
2 - Test the water for the chlorine level
3 - Wash your hands "thoroughly", then submerge two fingers all the way into the glass of water for sixty seconds.
4 - After sixty seconds remove your fingers and test the glass of water again for chlorine (you might be shocked).

No, the chlorine didn't evaporate. It was absorbed into the skin. Consider what the American Journal of Public Health. Skin absorption has been underestimated and it might even be the primary route of exposure of contaminants in drinking water.

Types of water supplies

1. Public Water System
   Public water systems are broken down into two categories:
   1 - Community water systems which serve the same people 12 months a year. Most individuals are served by community water systems.
   2 - Non-Community Water Systems which does not serve the same people year round.
   There are two types of non-community systems:
   A - A non-community water system is one that serves the same people more than six months of the year, but not year-round. For example a school with its own water supply in considered a non-transient system.
   B - A non community water system that serves the public but not the same individuals for more than six months. For example a rest area, camp ground, etc.

Community water systems are generally owned and operated by the village, city or town, in other words the municipality itself. This type of water system must meet EPA standards for certain contaminants and filtration.

Privately owned water supplies are owned by a private or public company, which can sell the water to the village (who in turn sells the water to the residents and businesses) or they might sell the water directly to the residents and businesses. This type of water supply must meet EPA standards for certain contaminants and filtration.

2. Individual Wells or Individual Water Supplies

These are exactly what they sound like. The age old process of digging or drilling a hole into the ground until water is hit then using a pump to bring the water to the surface. In days gone by and possibly still in remote areas of the country the water is brought to the surface via a bucket on a rope lowered down the well shaft. This type of water supply has no EPA standards for contaminants and filtration. An individual well offers NO specific filtration for chemicals or bacteria infestation that might be present in the water source. Some of the most common contaminants can be fecal matter, bacteria, pesticides and insecticides, industrial wastewater or leakage and chemicals from streets, driveways and parking lots which have run off into waterways or seeped into the ground water supplies which are tapped by individual wells.

Individual river/stream water
These types of water supplies generally pump the water directly from a stream or river in close proximity. In the old days (and again possibly in remote areas around the country) people would fill buckets directly from these sources. This type of water supply has no EPA standards for contaminants and filtration. An individual water supply source direct from a river or stream offers NO specific filtration for chemicals or bacteria infestation that has seeped into the water. Some of the most common contaminants can be fecal matter, bacteria, pesticides and insecticides, industrial wastewater or leakage, and chemicals from streets, driveways and parking lots which have run off into waterways or seeped into the ground water supplies.

The use of pesticides, insecticides, most chemical toxins from industry wastewater, PCB's and numerous other chemicals didn't exist back a hundred years ago (at least not to the degree they do know). These contaminants pose a threat to our drinking water supply because they can not always be filtered through a public water system.

There are several different sources where Public water systems can get their water supply:

1. Rivers/Streams
2. Lakes
3. Reservoirs
4. Ponds
5. Wells
   A. Deep
   B. Shallow

The most common way public water systems filter contaminants in our water supply is the same as it was 100 years ago. Most systems use a multi stage filtration process, consisting of adding, a chemical coagulate to help the sediment drop to the bottom of the filter tanks. The water then progresses through a filtering process of "sand and gravel". This is basically a swimming pool filter. Anyone familiar with swimming pools knows that this process is not designed to remove bacteria or chemical contaminants. It is designed to remove sediment. Some systems might add a carbon powder to deal with unpleasant taste. The systems then generally add a combination of other "strong chemicals" to our drinking water. Most public water systems add fluoride which was originally added to help prevent cavities in children. This has met up with very strong opposition including the EPA's own scientist, engineers and their unions representing 7,000 employees (see fluoride section).

Most systems also add chlorine as a disinfectant. Unfortunately, Chlorine is not a fool proof disinfectant against all bacteria, which was unfortunately discovered when over 400,000 people got sick and over 100 people died from a Cryptosporidium out break in Milwaukee, Wisconsin about 12 years ago. Chlorine has also met up with strong opposition from the EPA itself stating that chlorine when combined with other chemicals in the drinking water can produce PCBs. The EPA states: Some epidemiological studies have shown a link between bladder, rectal, and colon cancers as well as DBP exposure. (see Chlorine in the Chemical section)

Most public water systems also add "strong" chemicals to the water, not as a disinfectant, but to stop lead in the water pipes from leaching into the water. Lead was used in the water piping system to deliver the water from the facility to the individual homes and businesses throughout the village or town. Most of those pipes are still in existence around the country. The chemicals that are added are designed to coat the pipes so lead doesn't break away from the inside of the pipes and make there way to the homes and businesses in the area. Unfortunately, this is not a fool proof approach and there have been lead detected in multiple homes on blocks or areas due to the lead leaching from the public water systems pipes. There are also numerous cases of lead leaching into water from the plumbing inside the homes itself.

Is Bottled Water the Answer?

One of the biggest considerations with bottled water is that it is NOT regulated by the EPA, but by the FDA on a federal level.

➢ First, the belief that all drinking water is totally safe, pure, or filtered and better than tap water is wrong. Whether it is labeled as "Pure," "Refined" or "Spring" water, there could be surprises.

➢ Approximately 40% of all bottled water comes from a public water system, just like kitchen tap water. - - As shocking as that statement is, that might be the good news. At least Public water systems, offer some type of filtration and disinfection and generally have stricter EPA regulations to follow than FDA bottled water regulations.

➢ It's estimated that over 60% of all bottled water is exempt from FDA bottled water regulations. This is due to the Federal regulation criteria. The FDA regulations come into force when a Bottled water company bottles water in one state and sells it in a different state (in other words the water crossed state lines). What bottle water companies can do is simply have a bottling water facility in that state and they can avoid FDA bottle water Regulations and will fall under state regulations.

➢ The University of Arizona conducted a study on vending machine water. These were vending machines that "fill" the customers empty bottles with water, not vending machines that dispense a full, sealed bottle of water (like soda machines). Vending machines that dispense drinking water are becoming more popular among people distrustful of tap water. The customer brings their bottle from home, puts in their money and takes home a full bottle of what they think is pure water. The study found bacteria in close to one out of four of the supermarket vending machines tested. This is due to people, children, etc. touching the water dispenser spout on the machine and transferring bacteria and germs from their hands to the water dispenser spout. Maybe you have heard of a recent study which stated there are more germs or bacteria on a shopping cart handle than you would ever believe. The germs from a persons hand, sick child, etc. are easily transferred to the water dispenser spout on the drinking water vending machine.

Following are some of the differences in EPA tap water regulations and FDA Bottled water regulations:

- Remember the EPA does not regulate the bolted water industry the FDA does on a federal level. The EPA states City tap water can have NO confirmed E.Coli or Fecal Coliform Bacteria. The FDA bottled water regulations DOES NOT state that Bottled water can have NO confirmed E.Coli or Fecal Coliform Bacteria.

- According to EPA regulations water coming from a municipal water system going to the public MUST be disinfected and filtered. The FDA bottled water regulations have NO regulations for disinfecting and filtering bottled water.

Following is an extreme case of bottle water labeling:
A Bottled water company which sold their water as "Spring Water" was being bottled from a well at a facility next to a hazardous waste site. Testing of the water showed it contained contaminants from industrial chemicals. It was determined that the bottled water labeling as "Spring Water" was not

misleading because the water at times did come to the surface on its own a short distance away from the well. The facility was eventually closed.

What can be in bottled water? Depending on the water bottling source, it could contain the same chemicals as tap water, or even worse! If the bottled water is being bottled from a municipal water system source, it will probably contain chlorine, fluoride, and possibly other chemicals which have entered the water supply (as stated earlier from the EPA - storm water runoff, acid rain, septic system leakage, industrial waste water, etc.). If the water is being bottled from a "Spring" you should identify where the source actually is. Does it contain E.Coli?, Fecal Coliform Bacteria? Nitrates? Radium 226 and 228? Keep in mind that both individual wells and municipal water systems have been identified to contain radium 226 & 228 or radon in their drinking water at levels higher than the Maximum Contaminant Level set by the EPA.

The FDA is doing the best they can to regulate the industry, but it is growing by leaps and bounds. Some reports show the bottled water industry had sales of over $30,000,000,000 in 2005. Who would have thought 20 years ago people would be spending $1, $2 and even over $3 for a bottle of water?

There are numerous types of bottled water on the market. In fact a substantial amount of companies actually bottle water using different filtration methods or none at all. We have seen a company sell water with a Reverse Osmosis filtration process and other bottles with the same label which were not bottled with the same filtration methods. Confusing? Yes, it is. If you are going to buy bottled water, I highly recommend you buy water that has been filtered through a Reverse Osmosis process or distilled bottled water. Be careful not all bottled water is filtered or disinfected.

Individual Private Wells or Private Drinking Supplies

Water supplies from private wells, rivers, streams or lakes are at more risk now than at any other time in the history of our country. A private well or private water offers no filtration or disinfection against any bacteria, chemicals or impurities. As the EPA has stated in their "Biggest Threats to Our Water Supply" (and has been published by numerous media outlets most recently the Chicago Sun Times), contaminants and chemicals can in fact seep through the ground into an aquifer where well water is pumped from. Rivers, streams and lakes can be contaminated with chemicals from industrial waste water or acid rain. The position of "acid rain" by the EPA puts every single water source at risk for containing contaminants. As we have seen with natural disasters and volcano eruptions the pollution can travel hundreds and even a thousand miles in the atmosphere. So when rain water falls to earth it can pick up some of these contaminants and bring them back down to earth. These contaminants can fall to the earth and end up in rivers, streams, lakes and the soil. Water run off after a heavy rain or snow melting can collect contaminants from the ground and deliver them to other water sources such as the rivers, creeks and lakes. They might also soak into the soil and work their way down to the water supply.

What is a good depth for a well?

This is one of the most important questions you will get answered regarding your private well. I have heard of too many stories about people bragging that they hit water 15 feet or 20 feet from the surface. The closer your water source to the ground the MORE contaminants can enter it. Consider a simple analogy. More contaminants, chemicals and bacteria can absorb into a 15 or 20 feet deep well water source than a water supply source that's 100 feet or 200 feet deep. However, having a 200 foot deep well doesn't guarantee safety. The Radium problem we discussed earlier is basically involving municipal water systems which are over 1,000 feet deep. Private Wells can encounter contaminants whether they are 15 feet deep or 1,500 feet deep. Considering radon and radium are both a form of radiation that are both found in the ground. When a well is dug and taps into a water source, that source of water could contain radon or radium.

Another problem is chemicals, when a well taps into an underground water source it is generally not a boxed in underground pond. It is generally an underground traveling water source, which can cover miles and miles. This is both good news and potentially bad news. The bad news is contaminants and chemicals can be entering your water supply source miles and miles away. This is where people hear stories about toxic waste dumps, land fills, or chemical storage leakages miles away from homes contaminating a water supply source servicing dozens, hundreds, or even thousands of people.

Chlorination of a well does not filter or address any contaminants or chemicals which might exist in a well's water supply source; it is to address potential bacteria in the water.

The water quality association stresses the chlorination or shocking of private wells annually or every other year depending on the water source. Please follow the directions carefully on this process.

You should get updated information regarding "Well Shocking" or "Well Chlorination" or have a reputable licensed company conduct the procedure (following is a basic overview of the process and some common mistakes to avoid). Most companies and agencies recommend using common household bleach to chlorinate a private well. The amount of bleach used depends on the size of your well pipe and the depth. You should contact the company that installed the well for this information.
The basic procedures are as follows:

Some PRE steps:

> If you are using a water softener make sure you have the water softener By-Pass Valve engaged. The bleach will damage the media resin inside the water softener tank and could render it useless. If your water softener does not have a By-Pass Valve, you will have to contact a plumber to install the valve.

1 Carefully remove the well cap. Use sterile gloves as to not have any bacteria or germs from your hand contaminating the inside of the well cap. Be very cautious of a hard to remove well cap, it could be a sign of pressure. Carefully place the well cap on a clean surface.

2 Carefully pour the calculated amount of bleach down the well shaft.

3 Carefully place the well cap back on the well pipe shaft.

4 Making sure the water softener is bypassed; turn on a faucet until you smell the bleach in the water, then turn off that faucet. Repeat this process with EVERY faucet in the house and outside. Flush the toilets a few times to get bleached water into the toilet tank.

5 Allow the bleached water to sit in the pipes for a few hours. The longer the better (up to 6 or 8 hours is recommended).

6 After allowing the bleached water to sit in the pipes for several hours its time to flush it from the pipes.

7 If you have a septic system DO NOT drain the bleached water down the drain. A recommended procedure is to hook up a garden hose to an outside faucet and run it down the driveway to the street. Run the water until there is NO noticeable smell of bleach. Then turn on each faucet inside the house and allow them to run a few minutes to flush out any bleach remaining in the pipes (this small amount will not hurt the septic system). You should also flush all toilets a

few times. DO NOT forget to run a couple of dishwasher and washing machine cycles to flush the bleach through them. You do not have to let them run through an entire wash cycle. Just run them to fill up the machine and then drain it. Repeat this process until there is <u>No</u> smell of bleach in the water.

Private Wells and Public Water System wells

Keep in mind a well is a well, it is getting its water from an underground source. We like to think that water source is protected and as clean and pure as the day the earth was created. Unfortunately, that is not the case anymore.

I've heard way to many people with the belief that contaminants can not soak through the soil into their well. Consider the following situations.. There are countless wells which have been abandoned for one reason or another and have been damaged, cracked or missing well caps. This allows any and all contaminants to enter the well shaft and the water source itself. Contaminants on the ground, such as bacteria, E.Coli, fecal coliform bacteria, chemicals, solvents, etc. which are on streets, yards, farms, fields, etc. can be washed away with heavy rains and travel for miles and miles. When this contaminated water passes a damaged well cap, any possible contaminant can enter the well and those water sources. Most underground water sources have some type of exposure to the surface. In fact the accepted definition of "Spring Bottled Water" is water that makes its way to the surface on its own at some point and time. This makes the underground water source completely exposed to any and all contaminants at the surface.

The accepted position in well digging is the deeper the well the better. This is because it is assumed the deeper the water source the less contaminants have worked their way down through the ground into it. This is not always true, especially when you consider the water could be laced with Radon and Radium.

Filtration Devices and Equipment

I am not going to recommend any specific water filtration or conditioning types of systems in this book. The reason is the constant introduction of new or improved systems. We could not possibly contact everyone after we have tested a new or improved system with our recommendations. What we suggest is that you visit: www.drinkingwaterinfo.com to get updated information on what water filtration and conditioning systems we recommend. There is also a special offer on the last page of this book.

Hard Water

When most people think of hard water they think of a water softener. Water Softeners are not filtration systems. They are designed to deal with hard water – excessive amounts of calcium. Hard water is not a dangerous contaminant, it is just a nuisance. Calcium due to its molecular structure bonds to almost anything it touches, this includes shower walls, bathtubs, sinks, faucets, and the inside of hot water tanks, pipes and plumbing fixtures. Hard water will cause premature breakdown of everything it touches.

Studies have stated that hard water can shorten the lifespan of certain household appliances. Following premature breakdown schedules for water related appliances calculated at an EPA Hard Water Level of "7" (this is estimated to be the average hard water level in the United States):
Hot Water Tank = 50%
Washing Machine = 50%
Dish Washer = 30%
Plumbing Fixtures = 50%
Washable Clothing = 15% - 20%

The studies estimate that hard water costs the average family of four between $30 and $50 a month due to future dollars spent on premature breakdown of water related appliances and clothing.

Following is the EPA Hard Water Scale:

Grains Per Gallons	Milligrams Per Liter	Rating
Less than 1	Less than 17.1	Soft
1 to 3.5	17.1 to 60	Slightly Hard
3.5 to 7	60 to 120	Moderately Hard
7 to 10.5	120 to 180	Hard
Over 10.5	Over 180	Very Hard

Most companies use the Grains per Gallons basis

How do you know if you have hard water? One simple question will help you determine the answer. If you do not wipe down your shower walls for a few days after showering, will you have to use strong soap or cleaners to remove the soap scum? If so you probably have hard water. If you have had a plumbing fixture, or appliance repaired or replaced recently (that has been in use for a few years) what did it look like? Was there a scale build up inside the pipe or fixture or were the walls of the pipes, completely clean? Scale build up is a sign of hard water. Another way is by laundry soap consumption. If it takes an entire cup of laundry detergent or more to do a standard size load of laundry, you probably have hard water. The additional soap and phosphates in the detergent are needed to cut through the calcium and magnesium in the water.

To give you an idea of hard water levels, here in the Chicago, Illinois area, the water comes from Chicago (Lake Michigan) and services millions and millions of people throughout the area. The water hardness is at about 11 to 12 Grains per Gallon, which is off the EPA chart. I want to stress hard water is not dangerous, it is a nuisance. The further outlying areas of Chicago have water ranging up to 30 Grains per Gallon and higher.

Water Softeners:
Water softener technology has not really changed in the last 50 years. Except they now use a computer control valve on the top to automatically regenerate the unit.

Water softeners work via a process called ion exchange. The system consists of a tank filled with media resin which exchanges the calcium ions for sodium ions as they pass by the media resin. There is a separate salt tank which is generally filled with salt (sodium) or potassium; this is called the Brine tank and brine solution. The brine tank is usually a separate pvc tank or can be included within the outer housing of the water softener tank (on less expensive units). After a set calculated number of days, the system will regenerate itself. This includes a back flushing of the water softener tank and then filling the water softener tank with the brine solution (salt water). The brine solution soaks in the water softener tank for generally a few hours. This process is used for the ion exchange, where the calcium deposits which have stuck to the media resin are exchanged for the sodium Ions which are in the brine solution which was flushed into the water softener tank during regeneration.

The system is then rinsed out with "clean water" (I use the term "clean water" loosely because the water that is being used to rinse out the water softener tank is the exact same water coming in from outside that you are trying to soften in the first place) and the water is washed down the drain.

One of the side effects of a water softener is the amount of sodium left in the water softener tank. Most people can taste the salt residue in the water after it regenerates (which effects the taste of drinking water, coffee, tea, soups and any food cooked with water). The remaining excess salt (sodium) in the water softener tank can also be a concern for individuals on special diets, such as people with high blood pressure, heart conditions, etc. The water softening companies state the amount of salt remaining in the tanks is minimal, but test we have conducted on some systems have shown levels of sodium were over 10 times the amount of sodium compared to not using the water softener.

There are also potential interactions with water softeners. Some contaminants even secondary contaminants can hinder the effectiveness or even ruin the water softener completely. Iron is one of a water softener media resins worst enemies. Any amount of iron in the water can clog up a water softener media resin. The iron puts a coating over the media resin as it washes over it. Eventually, the iron can completely cover the media resin turning it into one big hunk of a gooey glob (that's the technical term), completely rendering the water softener useless. Most water softener companies will warranty their water softeners up to a certain level of iron, generally 1ppm or 2 ppm. However, since iron levels can fluctuate up or down, it also acts as a loop hole for a water softeners warranty which generally reads "if the level of iron exceeds the maximum level of "x" the warranty is completely void.

There are water softener systems that can handle up to 3ppm and even to 5 ppm of iron depending on the ph in the water (see www.drinkingwaterinfo.com for further information).

"First, soft water is more likely to dissolve certain metals from pipes than hard water. These metals include cadmium and lead, which are potentially dangerous. Second, soft water may be a significant source of sodium for those who need to restrict their sodium intake"
(Center for Disease Control ws–Colorado State University) (40)

Reverse Osmosis Systems (R/O Systems)

A standard reverse osmosis system (R/O) works by forcing the water through a membrane. Depending on the type of membrane used in the R/O System it can provide one of the best forms of drinking water filtration in the world.

Not all reverse osmosis systems are created equal. Some only offer 2 or 3 stage filtration, while the higher quality models can offer 5 and 6 stages. The stages are not the only consideration when selecting a reverse osmosis (R/O) system.

The size and type of filters used and their filtering ability is another big consideration when looking at a R/O System. It is important for it to match the types of contaminants you might have in your water and make sure you have good quality filters so you don't have to change them every month.

Smaller 2 or 3 stage R/O Systems can be either counter top versions or under the counter versions. The better quality 5 and 6 stage units will almost always be under the counter models. The 6th stage is generally an ultra violet light. This is extremely important for individuals on a private individual well or getting their water from an unprotected and unfiltered source. The ultra violet light is in our opinion one of the best ways of addressing potential bacteria in the water.

R/O Systems are used for drinking and cooking water purposes and not generally for whole house filtration. This is because of the amount of time it takes to generate one gallon of refined water. The average bath tub might hold 24 gallons of water while the average washing machine could use 55 to 60 gallons of water to complete one load of laundry. Even a good residential R/O system can not keep up with that demand in a matter of minutes.

There are also different types of membranes used in R/O Systems. This can make a big difference in the rejection rate of contaminants and the quality of the water coming out of the system. R/O system's filtering ability is described in "rejection rates" rather than "filtering ability". Refection rates apply to the "amount" or "percentage" a given contaminant will be rejected. For example, there are R/O Systems on the market that will reject 99% of a particular contaminant while a "similar looking" R/O System (in fact it might even look better) might only reject 60% of the exact same contaminant. Which means 40% of that particular contaminant was not rejected by the R/O Membrane and made its way into your drinking water.

Another big consideration is the amount of time it takes to regenerate one gallon of refined water. Nothing will be a bigger waste of your money, than a fancy looking cheap Reverse Osmosis System. Some Reverse Osmosis Systems on the Market can take 2 to 3 hours to regenerate a gallon of water. This will get frustrating very quickly. You make a pot of pasta, or soup, and then you want to make some lemonade for the kids and nothing happens when you turn on the tap. No water comes out. The reason is most companies use small 1 to 1 ½ gallon storage tanks. When that tank is emptied you now face the frustration of waiting for up to 2 and 3 hours just to get another gallon of refined water. This is what makes so many people so frustrated, that they actually start buying bottled water again so they have some water on hand. There are Reverse Osmosis systems on the market that can provide tremendous filtration capabilities, high rejection rates of contaminants, larger storage units (3 to 3 ½ gallons) and the ability of regenerating a gallon of refined water in less than 15 minutes.

With a properly selected Reverse Osmosis System you will have years of a plentiful supply of refined drinking and cooking water.

R/O Systems are probably the best at eliminating most Total Dissolved Solids (TDS). You can see a great visual TDS test at: www.drinkingwaterinfo.com. The test consist of using two water samples. One glass is filled with ordinary tap water, the other glass is filled with water from the office's R/O system faucet. The test uses an electrical meter which sends a current through two probes inserted into both glasses of water. This basically causes a burning effect on any contaminants in the water. The visual results of this are shocking.

Faucet attachment filters
Most people have seen the filters for sale on the shelf at their local hardware store or even food store. They screw onto the kitchen faucet spout and help to filter certain chemicals from the water. The biggest problem is their size and filtering capacity. These types of filters can break down earlier than expected and actually account for higher TDS levels in the drinking water. They have a limited amount of filtering ability and I personally believe they give a homeowner a false sense of security.

Charcoal and/or Carbon filters
By themselves they provide some filtering ability for chemicals but not as broad of a filtering spectrum as when used in conjunction with a Reverse Osmosis system.

Refrigerator Drinking Water/Ice Makers
Most refrigerators made in the last ten years or so with water and ice dispensers have filters. These filters should be changed every 6 months to one year. I have only met a hand full of people who have ever changed that filter. Can you imagine the condition and contaminants on that filter? Every refrigerator water or ice dispenser I have ever checked had a higher TDS level than water coming from the kitchen faucet. This brings up the issue of ice cubes. What ever is in the drinking water is in the ice cubes. You should consider a separate ice making filter.

Ozonination Filters

Ozonination systems are designed to address bacteria in water. An Ozone system by itself is not designed to filter or address other contaminants in the water such as chemicals. I have done much research on these units and at this time I am not in favor of them. I am not a believer in adding chemicals, toxins, or other outside material to the water just to get rid of a contaminant. I believe the best way of refining water is through removing the contaminant by using proper filtration.

An Ozone-destroying device is needed at the exhaust of the ozone-reactor to prevent toxicity and fire hazards. It may produce undesirable aldehydes and ketones by reacting with certain organics. It will not oxidize some refactory organics or will oxidize too slowly to be of practical signicance. Groundwater systems that have iron levels above 0.1 milligrams per liter may have iron complaints if ozonation or chlorination is added.
(West Virginia University WS - The National Drinking Water Clearing House) (41)

Whole House filters

Whole House filters generally have a replaceable filter cartridge. They are installed at the point of entry of the water pipe just inside the house. They come in different sizes and different filtering abilities. If you are on a private well, you will want a filter that can remove sediment. If you are on municipal water you will want a filter to remove chlorine and VOC's. This type of filter will remove the chlorine and VOC's from all faucets at the house (bathtubs and showers - they will not replace a complete drinking water system). The micron filtering rating is of extreme importance along with the filter's lifespan.

One of the biggest problems with most filters is their micron rating. The smaller the rating the more they will filter, BUT, the faster they get clogged and need to be replaced.

Contaminant Filtration Spectrum

This Filtration Spectrum is based on high quality filtration devices. Some filtration devices even though they may be similar or classified in the same category may not have the same filtration abilities as what is shown in the chart.

CONTAMINANTS	Activated Carbon Filters (Granular)	Twin Stage (Activated Carbon Block and Sediment)	Disinfection - UV light -	6 Stage Reverse Osmosis System	Anoin Exchange	Airation	Distillation
Asbestos				X			X
Benzene	X	X		X(*)		X	X*
Copper				X			X
Chlorine	X			X			
Fluoride				X			X
Lead				X			X
Atrazine	X	X		X			X*
Coliform Bacteria			X	(x) w/uv light			
Mercury	X	X		X	X		X
Arsenic				X	X		X
Sulfate				X	X		X

Trichloroethylene	X	X		X(*)			X
Radium				X	X		X
Radon	X			X(*)	X	X	X*
Nitrate				X	X		X
Cryptosporidium Parvum			X	X			X
Sulvate				X	X		X
Zinc				X			X
Total Dissolved Solids				X			X
Metallic Taste				X			X
Objectionable Taste	X			X			X
Sediment		X		X			X
Objectionable Odor	X		x	X(*)			
Color	X			X	X		X

x – with added filtration assistance from carbon filters

Public Water Systems EPA Violations
Reported and Non-Reported

One of the surprising things we found was the number of "non reported" violations on the EPA violation reports. This means the water supply source did not submit or conduct the required testing for contaminants.

The Washington Post Article as reported on MSNBC on October 4, 2004 states that: many of the major city public water systems have been deceptive, or even fraudulent in their reporting of the problems (Maximum Contaminant Level Violations).

In 2001, one out of every four community water systems did not conduct testing or report the results for all of the monitoring required to verify the safety of their drinking water. (EPA) (42)

The EPA places the following NOTICE on every Safe Drinking Water Information System Violation Report available to the public:
NOTICE: EPA is aware of inaccuracies and underreporting of some data in the Safe Drinking Water Information System. We are working with the states to improve the quality of the data. The EPA knows that some public water systems are underreporting violations.

After reviewing thousands of pages of documents we were able to locate the information source for the violations statistics. The most recent statistics were released in October 2005 for the year of 2003. In 2003 there were 14,435 health based violations from water supply systems reported to the EPA's division of SDWIS/FED. The total of health based violations in 2002 reported to the EPA was 14,028
(David De John –Clean Water Institute) (43)

A health based violation means either that the system has exposed its users to what EPA has judged as an unreasonable risk of illness, or that the system has filled to treat its water to the extent EPA has judged necessary to protect its users from an unreasonable risk of illness.

(EPA) (44)

EPA Regulated Contaminants

Microorganisms

Contaminant	MCLG[1] (mg/L)[2]	MCL or TT[1] (mg/L)[2]	Potential Health Effects from Ingestion of Water	Sources of Contaminant in Drinking Water
Cryptosporidium (pdf file)	zero	TT[3]	Gastrointestinal illness (e.g., diarrhea, vomiting, cramps)	Human and fecal animal waste
Giardia lamblia	zero	TT[3]	Gastrointestinal illness (e.g., diarrhea, vomiting, cramps)	Human and animal fecal waste
Heterotrophic plate count	n/a	TT[3]	HPC has no health effects; it is an analytic method used to measure the variety of bacteria that are common in water. The lower the concentration of bacteria in drinking water, the better maintained the water system is.	HPC measures a range of bacteria that are naturally present in the environment
Legionella	zero	TT[3]	Legionnaire's Disease, a type of pneumonia	Found naturally in water; multiplies in heating systems

Contaminant	MCLG	MCL	Health Effects	Sources
Total Coliforms (including fecal coliform and E. Coli)	zero	5.0%[4]	Not a health threat in itself; it is used to indicate whether other potentially harmful bacteria may be present[5]	Coliforms are naturally present in the environment; as well as feces; fecal coliforms and E. coli only come from human and animal fecal waste.
Turbidity	n/a	TT[3]	Turbidity is a measure of the cloudiness of water. It is used to indicate water quality and filtration effectiveness (e.g., whether disease-causing organisms are present). Higher turbidity levels are often associated with higher levels of disease-causing microorganisms such as viruses, parasites and some bacteria. These organisms can cause symptoms such as nausea, cramps, diarrhea, and associated headaches.	Soil runoff
Viruses (enteric)	zero	TT[3]	Gastrointestinal illness (e.g., diarrhea, vomiting, cramps)	Human and animal fecal waste

Disinfection Byproducts

Contaminant	MCLG[1] (mg/L)[2]	MCL or TT[1] (mg/L)[2]	Potential Health Effects from Ingestion of Water	Sources of Contaminant in Drinking Water
Bromate	zero	0.010	Increased risk of cancer	Byproduct of drinking water disinfection
Chlorite	0.8	1.0	Anemia; infants & young children: nervous system effects	Byproduct of drinking water disinfection
Haloacetic acids (HAA5)	n/a[6]	0.060	Increased risk of cancer	Byproduct of drinking water disinfection
Total Trihalomethanes (THMs)	none[7] ----- n/a[6]	0.10 ----- 0.080	Liver, kidney or central nervous system problems; increased risk of cancer	Byproduct of drinking water disinfection

Disinfectants

Contaminant	MRDLG[1] (mg/L)[2]	MRDL[1] (mg/L)[2]	Potential Health Effects from Ingestion of Water	Sources of Contaminant in Drinking Water
Chloramines (as Cl_2)	MRDLG=4[1]	MRDL=4.0[1]	Eye/nose irritation; stomach discomfort, anemia	Water additive used to control microbes
Chlorine (as Cl_2)	MRDLG=4[1]	MRDL=4.0[1]	Eye/nose irritation; stomach discomfort	Water additive used to control microbes
Chlorine dioxide (as ClO_2)	MRDLG=0.8[1]	MRDL=0.8[1]	Anemia; infants & young children: nervous system effects	Water additive used to control microbes

Inorganic Chemicals

Contaminant	MCLG[1] (mg/L)[2]	MCL or TT[1] (mg/L)[2]	Potential Health Effects from Ingestion of Water	Sources of Contaminant in Drinking Water
Antimony	0.006	0.006	Increase in blood cholesterol; decrease in blood sugar	Discharge from petroleum refineries; fire retardants; ceramics; electronics; solder
Arsenic	0[7]	0.010 as of 01/23/06	Skin damage or problems with circulatory systems, and may have increased risk of getting cancer	Erosion of natural deposits; runoff from orchards, runoff from glass & electronics production wastes
Asbestos (fiber >10 micrometers)	7 million fibers per liter	7 MFL	Increased risk of developing benign intestinal polyps	Decay of asbestos cement in water mains; erosion of natural deposits
Barium	2	2	Increase in blood pressure	Discharge of drilling wastes; discharge from metal refineries; erosion of natural deposits
Beryllium	0.004	0.004	Intestinal lesions	Discharge from metal refineries and coal-burning factories; discharge from electrical, aerospace, and defense industries
Cadmium	0.005	0.005	Kidney damage	

Contaminant	MCLG	MCL	Potential Health Effects	Sources of Contaminant
				natural deposits; discharge from metal refineries; runoff from waste batteries and paints
Chromium (total)	0.1	0.1	Allergic dermatitis	Discharge from steel and pulp mills; erosion of natural deposits
Copper	1.3	TT[8], Action Level=1.3	Short term exposure: Gastrointestinal distress Long term exposure: Liver or kidney damage People with Wilson's Disease should consult their personal doctor if the amount of copper in their water exceeds the action level	Corrosion of household plumbing systems; erosion of natural deposits
Cyanide (as free cyanide)	0.2	0.2	Nerve damage or thyroid problems	Discharge from steel/metal factories; discharge from plastic and fertilizer factories
Fluoride	4.0	4.0	Bone disease (pain and tenderness of the bones); Children may get mottled teeth	Water additive which promotes strong teeth; erosion of natural deposits; discharge from fertilizer and aluminum factories

Contaminant	MCLG	MCL	Potential Health Effects	Sources of Contaminant
		Action Level=0.015	mental development; children could show slight deficits in attention span and learning abilities Adults: Kidney problems; high blood pressure	erosion of natural deposits
Mercury (inorganic)	0.002	0.002	Kidney damage	Erosion of natural deposits; discharge from refineries and factories; runoff from landfills and croplands
Nitrate (measured as Nitrogen)	10	10	Infants below the age of six months who drink water containing nitrate in excess of the MCL could become seriously ill and, if untreated, may die. Symptoms include shortness of breath and blue-baby syndrome.	Runoff from fertilizer use; leaching from septic tanks, sewage; erosion of natural deposits
Nitrite (measured as Nitrogen)	1	1	Infants below the age of six months who drink water containing nitrite in excess of the MCL could become seriously ill and, if untreated, may die. Symptoms include shortness of breath and blue-baby syndrome.	Runoff from fertilizer use; leaching from septic tanks, sewage; erosion of natural deposits

Selenium	0.05	0.05	Hair or fingernail loss; numbness in fingers or toes; circulatory problems	Discharge from petroleum refineries; erosion of natural deposits; discharge from mines
Thallium	0.0005	0.002	Hair loss; changes in blood; kidney, intestine, or liver problems	Leaching from ore-processing sites; discharge from electronics, glass, and drug factories

Organic Chemicals

Contaminant	MCLG[1] (mg/L)[2]	MCL or TT[1] (mg/L)[2]	Potential Health Effects from Ingestion of Water	Sources of Contaminant in Drinking Water
Acrylamide	zero	TT[2]	Nervous system or blood problems; increased risk of cancer	Added to water during sewage/wastewater treatment
Alachlor	zero	0.002	Eye, liver, kidney or spleen problems; anemia; increased risk of cancer	Runoff from herbicide used on row crops
Atrazine	0.003	0.003	Cardiovascular system or reproductive problems	Runoff from herbicide used on row crops
Benzene	zero	0.005	Anemia; decrease in blood platelets; increased risk of cancer	Discharge from factories; leaching from gas storage tanks and landfills
Benzo(a)pyrene (PAHs)	zero	0.0002	Reproductive difficulties; increased risk of cancer	Leaching from linings of water storage tanks and distribution lines
Carbofuran	0.04	0.04	Problems with blood, nervous system, or reproductive system	Leaching of soil fumigant used on rice and alfalfa

Contaminant			Potential Health Effects	Sources
Carbon tetrachloride	zero	0.005	Liver problems; increased risk of cancer	Discharge from chemical plants and other industrial activities
Chlordane	zero	0.002	Liver or nervous system problems; increased risk of cancer	Residue of banned termiticide
Chlorobenzene	0.1	0.1	Liver or kidney problems	Discharge from chemical and agricultural chemical factories
2,4-D	0.07	0.07	Kidney, liver, or adrenal gland problems	Runoff from herbicide used on row crops
Dalapon	0.2	0.2	Minor kidney changes	Runoff from herbicide used on rights of way
1,2-Dibromo-3-chloropropane (DBCP)	zero	0.0002	Reproductive difficulties; increased risk of cancer	Runoff/leaching from soil fumigant used on soybeans, cotton, pineapples, and orchards
o-Dichlorobenzene	0.6	0.6	Liver, kidney, or circulatory system problems	Discharge from industrial chemical factories
p-Dichlorobenzene	0.075	0.075	Anemia; liver, kidney or spleen damage; changes in blood	Discharge from industrial chemical factories

Contaminant			Potential health effects	Sources of contaminant
1,2-Dichloroethane	zero	0.005	Increased risk of cancer	Discharge from industrial chemical factories
1,1-Dichloroethylene	0.007	0.007	Liver problems	Discharge from industrial chemical factories
cis-1,2-Dichloroethylene	0.07	0.07	Liver problems	Discharge from industrial chemical factories
trans-1,2-Dichloroethylene	0.1	0.1	Liver problems	Discharge from industrial chemical factories
Dichloromethane	zero	0.005	Liver problems; increased risk of cancer	Discharge from drug and chemical factories
1,2-Dichloropropane	zero	0.005	Increased risk of cancer	Discharge from industrial chemical factories
Di(2-ethylhexyl) adipate	0.4	0.4	Weight loss, liver problems, or possible reproductive difficulties.	Discharge from chemical factories
Di(2-ethylhexyl) phthalate	zero	0.006	Reproductive difficulties; liver problems; increased risk of cancer	Discharge from rubber and chemical factories
Dinoseb	0.007	0.007	Reproductive difficulties	

Contaminant	MCLG	MCL	Potential Health Effects	Sources of Contaminant in Drinking Water
Dioxin (2,3,7,8-TCDD)	zero	0.00000003	Reproductive difficulties; increased risk of cancer	Emissions from waste incineration and other combustion; discharge from chemical factories
Diquat	0.02	0.02	Cataracts	Runoff from herbicide use
Endothall	0.1	0.1	Stomach and intestinal problems	Runoff from herbicide use
Endrin	0.002	0.002	Liver problems	Residue of banned insecticide
Epichlorohydrin	zero	TT[2]	Increased cancer risk, and over a long period of time, stomach problems	Discharge from industrial chemical factories; an impurity of some water treatment chemicals
Ethylbenzene	0.7	0.7	Liver or kidneys problems	Discharge from petroleum refineries
Ethylene dibromide	zero	0.00005	Problems with liver, stomach, reproductive system, or kidneys; increased risk of cancer	Discharge from petroleum refineries

Contaminant	MCLG	MCL	Potential Health Effects	Sources
Glyphosate	0.7	0.7	Kidney problems; reproductive difficulties	Runoff from herbicide use
Heptachlor	zero	0.0004	Liver damage; increased risk of cancer	Residue of banned termiticide
Heptachlor epoxide	zero	0.0002	Liver damage; increased risk of cancer	Breakdown of heptachlor
Hexachlorobenzene	zero	0.001	Liver or kidney problems; reproductive difficulties; increased risk of cancer	Discharge from metal refineries and agricultural chemical factories
Hexachlorocyclopentadiene	0.05	0.05	Kidney or stomach problems	Discharge from chemical factories
Lindane	0.0002	0.0002	Liver or kidney problems	Runoff/leaching from insecticide used on cattle, lumber, gardens
Methoxychlor	0.04	0.04	Reproductive difficulties	Runoff/leaching from insecticide used on fruits, vegetables, alfalfa, livestock
Oxamyl (Vydate)	0.2	0.2	Slight nervous system effects	Runoff/leaching from insecticide used on apples, potatoes, and tomatoes

Contaminant	MCLG	MCL	Potential health effects	Sources of contaminant
Polychlorinated biphenyls (PCBs)	zero	0.0005	Skin changes; thymus gland problems; immune deficiencies; reproductive or nervous system difficulties; increased risk of cancer	Runoff from landfills; discharge of waste chemicals
Pentachlorophenol	zero	0.001	Liver or kidney problems; increased cancer risk	Discharge from wood preserving factories
Picloram	0.5	0.5	Liver problems	Herbicide runoff
Simazine	0.004	0.004	Problems with blood	Herbicide runoff
Styrene	0.1	0.1	Liver, kidney, or circulatory system problems	Discharge from rubber and plastic factories; leaching from landfills
Tetrachloroethylene	zero	0.005	Liver problems; increased risk of cancer	Discharge from factories and dry cleaners
Toluene	1	1	Nervous system, kidney, or liver problems	Discharge from petroleum factories
Toxaphene	zero	0.003	Kidney, liver, or thyroid problems; increased risk of cancer	Runoff/leaching from insecticide used on cotton and cattle

Contaminant			Health Effects	Sources
2.4.5-TP (Silvex)	0.05	0.05	Liver problems	Residue of banned herbicide
1.2.4-Trichlorobenzene	0.07	0.07	Changes in adrenal glands	Discharge from textile finishing factories
1.1.1-Trichloroethane	0.20	0.2	Liver, nervous system, or circulatory problems	Discharge from metal degreasing sites and other factories
1.1.2-Trichloroethane	0.003	0.005	Liver, kidney, or immune system problems	Discharge from industrial chemical factories
Trichloroethylene	zero	0.005	Liver problems; increased risk of cancer	Discharge from metal degreasing sites and other factories
Vinyl chloride	zero	0.002	Increased risk of cancer	Leaching from PVC pipes; discharge from plastic factories
Xylenes (total)	10	10	Nervous system damage	Discharge from petroleum factories; discharge from chemical factories

Radionuclides

Contaminant	MCLG[1] (mg/L)[2]	MCL or TT[1] (mg/L)[2]	Potential Health Effects from Ingestion of Water	Sources of Contaminant in Drinking Water
Alpha particles	none[7] --------- zero	15 picocuries per Liter (pCi/L)	Increased risk of cancer	Erosion of natural deposits of certain minerals that are radioactive and may emit a form of radiation known as alpha radiation
Beta particles and photon emitters	none[7] --------- zero	4 millirems per year	Increased risk of cancer	Decay of natural and man-made deposits of certain minerals that are radioactive and may emit forms of radiation known as photons and beta radiation
Radium 226 and Radium 228 (combined)	none[7] --------- zero	5 pCi/L	Increased risk of cancer	Erosion of natural deposits
Uranium	zero	30 ug/L as of 12/08/03	Increased risk of cancer, kidney toxicity	Erosion of natural deposits

65

Notes

[1] Definitions:

Maximum Contaminant Level (MCL) - The highest level of a contaminant that is allowed in drinking water. MCLs are set as close to MCLGs as feasible using the best available treatment technology and taking cost into consideration. MCLs are enforceable standards.

Maximum Contaminant Level Goal (MCLG) - The level of a contaminant in drinking water below which there is no known or expected risk to health. MCLGs allow for a margin of safety and are non-enforceable public health goals.

Maximum Residual Disinfectant Level (MRDL) - The highest level of a disinfectant allowed in drinking water. There is convincing evidence that addition of a disinfectant is necessary for control of microbial contaminants.

Maximum Residual Disinfectant Level Goal (MRDLG) - The level of a drinking water disinfectant below which there is no known or expected risk to health. MRDLGs do not reflect the benefits of the use of disinfectants to control microbial contaminants.

Treatment Technique - A required process intended to reduce the level of a contaminant in drinking water.

[2] Units are in milligrams per liter (mg/L) unless otherwise noted. Milligrams per liter are equivalent to parts per million.

[3] EPA's surface water treatment rules require systems using surface water or ground water under the direct influence of surface water to (1) disinfect their water, and (2) filter their water or meet criteria for avoiding filtration so that the following contaminants are controlled at the following levels:

- *Cryptosporidium:* (as of1/1/02 for systems serving >10,000 and 1/14/05 for systems serving <10,000) 99% removal.

- *Giardia lambia:* 99.9% removal/inactivation

- Viruses: 99.99% removal/inactivation

- *Legionella:* No limit, but EPA believes that if *Giardia* and viruses are removed/inactivated, *Legionella* will also be controlled.

- Turbidity: At no time can turbidity (cloudiness of water) go above 5 nephelolometric turbidity units (NTU); systems that filter must ensure that the turbidity go no higher than 1 NTU (0.5 NTU for conventional or direct filtration) in at least 95% of the daily samples in any month. As of January 1, 2002, turbidity may never exceed 1 NTU, and must not exceed 0.3 NTU in 95% of daily samples in any month.

- HPC: No more than 500 bacterial colonies per milliliter.

- Long Term 1 Enhanced Surface Water Treatment (Effective Date: January 14, 2005); Surface water systems or (GWUDI) systems serving fewer than 10,000 people must comply with the applicable Long Term 1 Enhanced Surface Water Treatment Rule provisions (e.g. turbidity standards, individual filter monitoring, *Cryptosporidium* removal requirements, updated watershed control requirements for unfiltered systems).

- Filter Backwash Recycling; The Filter Backwash Recycling Rule requires systems that recycle to return specific recycle flows through all processes of the system's existing conventional or direct filtration system or at an alternate location approved by the state.

[4] more than 5.0% samples total coliform-positive in a month. (For water systems that collect fewer than 40 routine samples per month, no more than one sample can be total coliform-positive per month.) Every sample that has total coliform must be analyzed for either fecal coliforms or *E. coli* if two consecutive TC-positive samples, and one is also positive for *E.coli* fecal coliforms, system has an acute MCL violation.

[5] Fecal coliform and *E. coli* are bacteria whose presence indicates that the water may be contaminated with human or animal wastes. Disease-causing microbes (pathogens) in these wastes can cause diarrhea, cramps, nausea, headaches, or other symptoms. These pathogens may pose a special health risk for infants, young children, and people with severely compromised immune systems.

[6] Although there is no collective MCLG for this contaminant group, there are individual MCLGs for some of the individual contaminants:

  - Trihalomethanes: bromodichloromethane (zero); bromoform (zero); dibromochloromethane (0.06 mg/L). Chloroform is regulated with this group but has no MCLG.

  - Haloacetic acids: dichloroacetic acid (zero); trichloroacetic acid (0.3 mg/L). Monochloroacetic acid, bromoacetic acid, and dibromoacetic acid are regulated with this group but have no MCLGs.

[7] MCLGs were not established before the 1986 Amendments to the Safe Drinking Water Act. Therefore, there is no MCLG for this contaminant.

[8] Lead and copper are regulated by a Treatment Technique that requires systems to control the corrosiveness of their water. If more than 10% of tap water samples exceed the action level, water systems must take additional steps. For copper, the action level is 1.3 mg/L, and for lead is 0.015 mg/L.

[9] Each water system must certify, in writing, to the state (using third-party or manufacturer's certification) that when acrylamide and epichlorohydrin are used in drinking water systems, the combination (or product) of dose and monomer level does not exceed the levels specified, as follows:

  - Acrylamide = 0.05% dosed at 1 mg/L (or equivalent)
  - Epichlorohydrin = 0.01% dosed at 20 mg/L (or equivalent)

National Secondary Drinking Water Regulations

National Secondary Drinking Water Regulations (NSDWRs or secondary standards) are non-enforceable guidelines regulating contaminants that may cause cosmetic effects (such as skin or tooth discoloration) or aesthetic effects (such as taste, odor, or color) in drinking water. EPA recommends secondary standards to water systems but does not require systems to comply. However, states may choose to adopt them as enforceable standards.

Contaminant	Secondary Standard
Aluminum	0.05 to 0.2 mg/L
Chloride	250 mg/L
Color	15 (color units)
Copper	1.0 mg/L
Corrosivity	noncorrosive

Fluoride	2.0 mg/L
Foaming Agents	0.5 mg/L
Iron	0.3 mg/L
Manganese	0.05 mg/L
Odor	3 threshold odor number
pH	6.5-8.5
Silver	0.10 mg/L
Sulfate	250 mg/L
Total Dissolved Solids	500 mg/L
Zinc	5 mg/L

Sample - EPA Public Water System Violation Reports

The name of the Public Water System has been removed

As mentioned earlier in the book:

The Washington Post reported after analyzing data gathered from the EPA that more than 274 major cities currently exceed the EPA's lead standards, and many of them have been deceptive, or even fraudulent in their reporting of the problems.
(NBC nightly news as aired on 10/5/2004)

The Washington Post reported that many of the major cities have been deceptive or even fraudulent in their reporting of problems. This is disturbing to me, to consider that employees of the Public Water System can be fraudulently underreporting data to the EPA. To explain how the system works, the Water Systems are on the honor system to report information to the EPA.

Note: The verbiage used halfway down the first page, it says:
NOTICE: EPA is aware of inaccuracies and underreporting of some data in the Safe Drinking Water Information System. We are working with the states to improve the quality of the data.

The following violation report has been limited to one year of violations. The actual report shows violations back to the beginning of reporting.

Violation Report

Primary Water Source Type	Population Served
Ground water	106221

Results are based on data extracted on OCT-14-2005

EPA is not aware that this water system's annual water quality report is available on the internet. For a copy contact the water system.

NOTICE: EPA is aware of inaccuracies and underreporting of some data in the Safe Drinking Water Information System. We are working with the states to improve the quality of the data.

The tables below list all violations that the state reported to EPA for this water system. Health-based violations are listed first, followed by monitoring, reporting, and other violations.

Health Based Violations: amount of contaminant exceeded safety standard (MCL) or water was not treated properly.

Type of Violation	Occured Between: Begin Date	Occured Between: End Date	Contaminant	Maximum Contaminant Level	Contaminant Level Found	Violation Code
MCL Average	APR-01-2005	JUN-30-2005	Combined Radium (-226 & -228)	5	23.3	5070891

Type of Violation	Occured Between: Begin Date	Occured Between: End Date	Contaminant	Maximum Contaminant Level	Contaminant Level Found	Violation Code
MCL, Average	APR-01-2005	JUN-30-2005	Gross Alpha, Excl. Radon & U	15	18.96667	5070892

Follow-up Action	Date of Response
St Public Notif received	JUL-29-2005
St Violation/Reminder Notice	JUL-08-2005
St Public Notif requested	JUL-08-2005
St BCA signed	AUG-02-2004
St Compliance Meeting conducted	FEB-09-2004
St Formal NOV issued	DEC-17-2003

Follow-up Action	Date of Response
St Public Notif received	JUL-29-2005
St Violation/Reminder Notice	JUL-08-2005
St Public Notif requested	JUL-08-2005
St BCA signed	AUG-02-2004
St Compliance Meeting conducted	FEB-09-2004
St Formal NOV issued	DEC-17-2003

Following is an example of the Consumer Confidence Report from a Water System. You can request a report from your municipality.

IMPORTANT INFORMATION

(This report must be printed in Landscape Orientation to prevent cutting off of text)

The following pages comprise the Annual Consumer Confidence Report (CCR) for your water system.

To download the CCR into your word processing program follow these steps (Remember you must have the document set up in Landscape Orientation):

- Choose Edit from the MENU.
- Choose Select All from the edit dropdown MENU, (it will highlight all the information).
- Choose Edit from the MENU, select Copy from the edit dropdown MENU.
- Open your word processing program.
- Choose Edit from the MENU, select Paste from the edit dropdown MENU and the information will transfer.

In order to meet all of the requirements of the CCR you **must** include the following additional information if it

73

pertains to your water system.

- If your supply purchases water from another source you are required to include the current CCR year's Regulated Contaminants Detected table from your source water supply.
- If your water system had any violations during the current CCR Calendar year you are required to include an explanation of the corrective action taken by the water system.
- If your water system is going to use the CCR to deliver a Public Notification, you must include the full public notice and return a copy of the CCR and Public Notice with the Public Notice Certification Form. This is in addition to the copy and certification form required by the CCR Rule.

Annual Drinking Water Quality Report

Annual Water Quality Report for the period of January 1 to December 31, 2005

This report is intended to provide you with important information about your drinking water and the efforts made by the COAL CITY water system to provide safe drinking water. The source of drinking water used by COAL CITY is Ground Water.

For more information regarding this report contact:

Name _____

Phone _____

Este in

forme contiene información muy importante sobre el agua que usted bebe. Tradúzcalo ó hable con alguien que lo entienda bien.

The sources of drinking water (both tap water and bottled water) include rivers, lakes, streams, ponds, reservoirs, springs, and groundwater wells. As water travels over the surface of the land or through the ground, it dissolves naturally-occurring minerals and, in some cases, radioactive material, and can pickup substances resulting from the presence of animals or from human activity.

Contaminants that may be present in source water include:

Microbial contaminants, such as viruses and bacteria, which may come from sewage treatment plants, septic systems, agricultural livestock operations and wildlife.

Inorganic contaminants, such as salts and metals, which can be naturally occurring or result from urban storm water runoff, industrial, or domestic wastewater discharges, oil and gas production, mining, or farming.

Pesticides and herbicides, which may come from a variety of sources such as agriculture, urban storm water runoff, and residential uses.

Organic chemical contaminants, including synthetic and volatile organic chemicals, which are by-products of industrial processes and petroleum production, and can also come from gas stations, urban storm water runoff, and septic systems.

Radioactive contaminants, which can be naturally-occurring or be the result of oil and gas production and mining activities.

Drinking water, including bottled water, may reasonably be expected to contain at least small amounts of some contaminants. The presence of contaminants does not necessarily indicate that water poses a health risk. More information about contaminants and potential health effects can be obtained by calling the EPA's Safe Drinking Water Hotline at (800) 426-4791.

In order to ensure that tap water is safe to drink, EPA prescribes regulations which limit the amount of certain contaminants in water provided by public water systems. FDA regulations establish limits for contaminants in bottled water which must provide the same protection for public health.

Source Water Assessment

A Source Water Assessment summary is included below for your convenience.

Based on information obtained in a Well Site Survey, published in 1992 by the Illinois EPA, seventeen potential sources or possible problem sites were identified within the survey area of Coal City wells. Furthermore, information provided by the Leaking Underground Storage Tank Section of the Illinois EPA indicated several additional sites with ongoing remediations which may be of concern. The Illinois EPA has determined that the Coal City Community Water Supply's source water is not susceptible to contamination. This determination is based on a number of criteria including: monitoring conducted at the wells, monitoring conducted at the entry point to the distribution system, and the available hydrogeologic data on the wells. The Illinois Environmental Protection Act provides minimum protection zones of 200 feet for Coal City's wells. These minimum protection zones are regulated by the Illinois EPA. To further minimize the risk to the groundwater supply, the Illinois EPA recommends that four additional activities be assessed. First, the village may wish to petition county and local officials to enact a "maximum setback zone" ordinance to further protect their water supply. These ordinances are authorized by the Illinois Environmental Protection Act and allow county and municipal officials the opportunity to provide additional protection up to a fixed distance, normally 1,000 feet, from their wells. Second, the village should explore the options of either properly abandoning the inactive well or retrofitting it for active use as a source of water supply. Inactive wells that are not properly abandoned can act as direct conduits for surficial contaminants into the aquifer and are considered "routes" under the Environmental Protection Act. Third, the water supply staff may wish to revisit their contingency planning documents. Contingency planning documents are a primary means to ensure that, through emergency preparedness, the village will minimize their risk of being without safe and adequate water. Finally, the water supply staff is encouraged to review their cross connection control program to ensure that it remains current and viable. Cross connections to either the water treatment plant (for example, at bulk water loading stations) or in the distribution system may negate all source water protection initiatives provided by the village.

2005 Regulated Contaminants Detected

Coliform Bacteria

Maximum Contaminant Level Goal	Total Coliform Maximum Contaminant Level	Highest No. of Positive	Fecal Coliform or E. Coli Maximum Contaminant Level	Total No. of Positive E. Coli or Fecal Coliform Samples	Violation	Likely Source Of Contamination
0	1 positive monthly sample	1	Fecal Coliform or E. Coli MCL: A routine sample and a repeat sample are total coliform positive, and one is also fecal coliform or E. coli positive	1	No	Naturally present in the environment · Edit

Lead and Copper

Date Sampled: 9/6/2005

Definitions:

Action Level (AL): The concentration of a contaminant which, if exceeded, triggers treatment or other requirements which a water system must follow.

Action Level Goal (ALG): The level of a contaminant in drinking water below which there is no known or expected risk to health. ALG's allow for a margin of safety.

Lead MCLG	Lead Action Level (AL)	Lead 90th Percentile	# Sites Over Lead AL	Copper MCLG	Copper Action Level (AL)	Copper 90th Percentile	# Sites Over Copper AL	Likely Source of Contamination
0	15 ppb	3.6 ppb	0	1.3 ppm	1.3 ppm	0.045 ppm	0	Corrosion of household plumbing systems; Erosion of natural deposits · Edit

Water Quality Test Results

Definitions: The following tables contain scientific terms and measures, some of which may require explanation.Maximum Contaminant Level (MCL): The highest level of a contaminant that is allowed in drinking water. MCL's are set as close to the Maxium Contaminant Level Goal as feasible using the best available treatment technology.Maximum Contaminant Level Goal (MCLG): The level of a contaminant in drinking water below which there is no known or expected risk to health. MCL's allow for a margin of safety.mg/l: milligrams per litre or parts per million - or one ounce in 7,350 gallons of water.ug/l: micrograms per litre or parts per billion - or one ounce in 7,350,000 gallons of water.na: not applicable.Avg: Regulatory compliance with some MCLs are based on running annual average of monthly samples.Maximum Residual Disinfectant Level (MRDL): The highest level of disinfectant allowed in drinking water.Maximum Residual Disinfectant Level Goal (MRDLG): The level of disinfectant in drinking water below which there is no known or expected risk to health. MRDLG's allow for a margin of safety.

Regulated Contaminants

Disinfectants & Disinfection By-Products	Collection Date	Highest Level Detected	Range of Levels Detected	MCLG	MCL	Units	Violation	Likely Source Of Contaminant	
TTHMs [Total Trihalomethanes]	8/8/2001	3.54	Not Applicable	N/A	80	ppb	No	By-product of drinking water disinfection	Edit
Chlorine	6/30/2005	0.952	0.68 - 0.952	MRDLG=4	MRDL=4	ppm	No	Water additive used to...	Edit

Inorganic Contaminants	Collection Date	Highest Level Detected	Range of Levels Detected	MCLG	MCL	Units	Violation	Likely Source Of Contaminant	
Fluoride	4/10/2003	1.14	Not Applicable	4	4	ppm	No	Erosion of natural deposits; Water additive...	Edit
Nitrate-Nitrite	10/20/2003	0.31	Not Applicable	10	10	ppm	No	Runoff from fertilizer use; Leaching from...	Edit
Nitrate (As N)	6/13/2005	0.73	Not Applicable	10	10	ppm	No	Runoff from fertilizer use; Leaching from...	Edit

Radioactive Contaminants	Collection Date	Highest Level Detected	Range of Levels Detected	MCLG	MCL	Units	Violation	Likely Source Of Contaminant	
Alpha Emitters (Adjusted)	2/23/2004	13.65	Not Applicable	0	15	pCi/l	No	Erosion of natural deposits	Edit

	Collection Date	Highest Level Detected	Range of Levels Detected	MCLG	MCL	Units	Violation	Likely Source Of Contaminant	
Alpha Emitters (Adjusted)	2/23/2004	13.65	Not Applicable	0	15	pCi/L	No	Erosion of natural deposits	Edit
Combined Radium	3/3/2005	10.07	2.38 - 10.07	0	5	pCi/L	No	Erosion of natural deposits	Edit
Combined Uranium	2/23/2004	1.6	Not Applicable	0	30	ppb	No	Erosion of natural deposits	Edit
Alpha Emitters	3/3/2005	9.2	Not Applicable	0	15	pCi/L	No	Erosion of natural deposits	Edit
State Regulated Contaminants	Collection Date	Highest Level Detected	Range of Levels Detected	MCLG	MCL	Units	Violation	Likely Source Of Contaminant	
Sodium There is not a state or federal MCL for sodium. Monitoring is required to provide information to consumers and health officials that are concerned about sodium intake due to dietary precautions. If you are on a sodium-restricted diet, you should consult a physician about this level of sodium in the water.	4/10/2003	441	Not Applicable	N/A	N/A	ppm	No	Erosion of naturally occuring deposits; used in water softener regeneration	Edit

Note: The state requires monitoring of certain contaminants less than once per year because the concentrations of these contaminants do not change frequently. Therefore, some of this data may be more than one year old.

U.S. Environmental Protection Agency

Safe Drinking Water Information System (SDWIS)

SDWIS

This script opens a separate window for reporting data errors

Violation Report

This script opens a separate window for reporting data errors

Primary Water Source Type	Population Served
Ground water	6189

Results are based on data extracted on OCT-14-2005

NOTICE: EPA is aware of inaccuracies and underreporting of some data in the Safe Drinking Water Information System. We are working with the states to improve the quality of the data.

Follow-up Action	Date of Response
St Public Notif received	JUL-19-2005
St Violation/Reminder Notice	JUL-08-2005
St Public Notif requested	JUL-08-2005
St BCA signed	MAR-11-2004
St Compliance Meeting conducted	FEB-03-2004
St Formal NOV issued	DEC-19-2003

Type of Violation	Occured Between: Begin Date	Occured Between: End Date	Contaminant	Maximum Contaminant Level	Contaminant Level Found	Violation Code
MCL Average	JAN-01-2005	MAR-31-2005	Combined Radium (-226 & -228)	5	18.8	5070444

Follow-up Action	Date of Response
St Public Notif received	APR-14-2005
St Violation/Reminder Notice	APR-08-2005
St Public Notif requested	APR-08-2005
St BCA signed	MAR-11-2004
St Compliance Meeting conducted	FEB-03-2004
St Formal NOV issued	DEC-19-2003

Violation	Begin Date	End Date		Contaminant Level		Found		Code
MCL Average	JAN-01-2005	MAR-31-2005	Gross Alpha, Excl. Radon & U	15		32.75		5070445

Follow-up Action	Date of Response
St Public Notif received	APR-14-2005
St Violation/Reminder Notice	APR-08-2005
St Public Notif requested	APR-08-2005
St BCA signed	MAR-11-2004
St Compliance Meeting conducted	FEB-03-2004
St Formal NOV issued	DEC-19-2003

Reference Sources:

(1) USA Today Special Report "How safe is your water?" October 21, 1998

(2) CNN September 2, 1996 - http://www.cnn.com/HEALTH/9609/02/nfm/water.quality/

(3) Center for Disease Control (CDC)

(4) EPA – Water On Tap what you need to know Page 4

(5) EPA – Water On Tap what you need to know Page 1

(6) David De John – Clean Water Institute Web Site

(7) NBC nightly news aired on 10/5/2004

(8) Printed on the cover of every EPA municipal water system violation report available to the public

(9) Time Magazine October 24, 2005 P-62

(10) Dr. William Hirzy, Vice President, Chapter 280 of the National Treasury Employees Union, EPA headquarters in Washington, D.C.)

(11) Environmental Protection Agency EPA – The Children's Healthline – Issue: Your child ask for a drink of water brochure – Volume 3, March 1999, Page – 4

(12) CDC - Surveillance for Waterborne-Disease Outbreaks --- United States, 1999—2000 – MMWR Surveillance Summaries November 22, 2002 / 51/(SS08);1-28 Abstract paragraph 4 Results..

(13) Center for Disease Control

(14) EPA/CDC/ATSDR – Tap into Prevention – Drinking Water Information for Health Care Providers Booklet. May 13, 2004 Page 7

(15) P:ubMEd.Com

(16) CNN – CNN.Com September 2, 1996 First of three part series.

(17) EPA/CDC/ATSDR – Tap into Prevention – Drinking Water Information for Health Care Providers Booklet. May 13, 2004, Page 8

(18) Baylor University Medical Center Proceedings *BUMC Proceedings* 2001;14:144-149 – Hazardous Materials

(19) Chicago Sun Times, July 28, 2006, Page 31

(20) Journal of Dental Research 66: 1056-60- Whitford GM. (1987). Fluoride in dental products: safety considerations.

(21) Journal of Dental Research 66: 1056-60- Whitford GM. (1987). Fluoride in dental products: safety considerations.

(22) Time Magazine October 24, 2005 P-62

(23) Dr. William Hirzy, Vice President, Chapter 280 of the National Treasury Employees Union, EPA Headquarters in Washington, D.C.

(24) EPA The Children's Helthline – Issue: Your child asks for a drink of water...Volume 3, March 1999

(25)   http:www.webhealthcentre.com/general/yc_hrchart.asp
(26)   NBC nightly news aired on 10/5/2004
(27)   EPA – Tap into Prevention Drinking water for Health Care
         Proviers Page 10
(28)   EPA Water On Tap what you need to know P 6
(29)   EPA Water on Tap what you need to know P 5
(30)   Illinois Department of Health Environmental Health Fact Sheet
         http://www.idph.state.il.us/envhealth/factsheets/NitrateFS.htm
(31)   American College of Sports Medicine News Release June 4,
         2004
(32)   EPA – Dr. Lance Wallace November 4, 1997 ISEA Newsletter
         Fall/November 1997 Page 12
(33)   EPA/CDC/ATSAR – Tap into Prevention - Drinking Water for
         Health Care Providers May 13, 2004 Page 10
(34)   EPA Water On Tap what you need to know P 9
(35)   United States Department of Interior – United States
         Geological Survey USGS – Fact Sheet 137-99 September 1999
(36)   Agency for Toxic Substances and Disease Registry – DTSDR –
         DTSDR – Case studies in environmental medicine course
         SS3405 –
(37)   EPA – Dr. Lance Wallace November 4, 1997 ISEA Newsletter
         Fall/November 1997 Page 12
(38)   American Journal of Public Health, VOl 74, Issue 5 479-484
(39)   Center for Disease Control ws–Colorado State University
         Service In Action, Drinking water quality and health, 9.307
         Published May 1991. Revised October 1992
(40)   West Virginia University WS - The National Drinking Water
         Clearinghouse Tech Brief 1999
         http://www.nesc.wvu.edu/ndwc/pdf/OT/TB/TB12_ozone.pdf
(41)   Environmental Protection Agency EPA – Water on Tap What
         you need to Know Booklet October 2003 Page – 3
(42)   Referenced material gathered from the 2003 National Public
         Water Systems Compliance Report – National Summary
         September 2005, Page 5
(43)   2003 National Public Water Systems Compliance Report –
         National Summary September 2005, Page 6
(44)   EPA - Drinking Water Priority Rulemaking: Microbial and
         Disinfection (Byproduct Rules)
         http://www.epa.gov/OGWDW/mdbp/mdbp.html

REBATE CERTIFICATE

David De John started Hydro Tech to conduct extensive research on water conditioning and filtration equipment. This offer is to help individuals who would like to provide their family with added protection from contaminants in the water with high quality filtration. This offer also allows you to avoid inflated prices due to sales commissions, and large overhead by retail stores.

This rebate is good for a $200 Mail in rebate on a Drinking water, hard water, whole house system Conditioning System purchased online by March 31, 2007.

Visit: www.drinkingwaterinfo.com

Rebate applies to the online purchase of any of the following:
1)   Hard Water Conditioning System
2)   6 Stage Reverse Osmosis Drinking Water System
3)   Whole House Chlorine and VOC filter

To receive the $200 rebate on any of the above systems, carefully remove this page from the book, complete all lines on the form below and mail it to Hydro Tech with a copy of your receipt. Rebate must be received by Hydro Tech within 30 days of the date of purchase of one of the above systems.

SPECIAL LIMITED OFFER:

Double your rebate to $400 by purchasing any two of the above Water conditioning or filtration systems online, from Hydro Tech. Both systems must be purchased at the same time and must be reflected on the Hydro Tech receipt to receive the double rebate offer.

Triple your rebate to $600 by purchasing all three of the above Water conditioning and filtration systems online from Hydro Tech. All three systems must be purchased at the same time and must be reflected on the Hydro Tech receipt to receive the triple rebate offer.

_____
Name

_____
Address   City

_____
State   Zip

System(s) Purchased: _____ Hard Water conditioning system
                              _____ 6 stage R/O Drinking water system
                              _____ Whole House Chlorine and VOC filter

Mail to: Hydro Tech / 6621 Linden Drive / Oak Forest, Illinois 60452

REBATE CERTIFICATE

See other side for details